MODERN MEDITATION:

Science and Shortcuts

Thomas Valone, PhD, PE

for Paramahansa Yogananda

Modern Meditation: Science and Shortcuts

Thomas F. Valone, PhD, PE

ISBN 978-1-935023-00-5

First Edition, 2008
Second Edition, 2009

Thanks to the Washington Post, Time magazine, Neuroscience, University of Kentucky, HD Lighthouse, Lorin Roche, Maharishi University and Self-Realization Fellowship for their contributions

Integrity Research Institute
5020 Sunnyside Avenue, Suite 209
Beltsville MD 20705
301-220-0440, 800-295-7674
FAX: 301-513-5728
Email: IRI@starpower.net
www.IntegrityResearchInstitute.org
author's curriculum vitae on website

Table of Contents

Preface

This book represents a personal journey that I am happy to share with the reader. From all of the *meditation* training seminars that I have led, it seems timely to finally put into print the main steps to achieving a major improvement in your mental outlook, ability, youthfulness, and peacefulness which meditation has proven to provide. Just look at the evidence with which I back up every suggested stage of meditation practice. You might find the combination of meditation instruction and scientific findings so convincing that you'll just have to adopt a new daily routine in your own life.

As a teenager back in 1967, I picked up a tiny book called *Metaphysical Meditations* by Paramahansa Yogananda which inspired me to try meditating, even if only with the guided meditations in the book, which I diligently dictated into my tape recorder for playback. A few years later, I bought the book, *The Science of Being and the Art of Living* by Maharishi Mahesh Yogi and read it from cover to cover. Shortly afterwards, I wrote to the publisher to find out where Transcendental Meditation (TM) was being taught and then in 1972 it was available in Buffalo NY for the first time.

On the day of my "initiation" into TM, I found that I was so peaceful that I skipped dinner that night, for the first time ever, to my mother's surprise. I also practiced TM daily for about three years and found lots of benefits, including overcoming a tendency to stutter when under stress, as well as a way to collect my thoughts and resolve issues of work, divorce, and school, all of which were overwhelming to a guy in his twenties. Then in 1975, I attended my first yoga retreat led by Amrit Desai from the Kripalu Yoga Ashram, as it was called. We met at Ursinus College in Pennsylvania during August for a full week. This yoga retreat introduced me to vegetarianism and kundalini yoga, as well as a three-day fast only on watermelon.

Many people there had unusual experiences and I remember feeling the electricity of my nerves on the right side of my brain one morning as I woke up, which was a peculiar and pleasant experience that also made sense to me since the right side of the brain is the image and nonverbal side that is most active during sleep and dreams. Near the end of the week, I realized that there had not been a cloud in the sky for the entire week at the retreat. As we gathered on the lawn of the college at 7 AM on Friday for Hatha Yoga exercises, forming three concentric circles with Yogi Desai in the middle, I noticed that a set of parallel clouds were forming in the distance in the sky. The person next to me also noticed this and as the parallel clouds formed four bars with a couple of shorter bars below, sort of left justified, my partner next to me, who was an ashram resident, said, "It looks like an I Ching." The formation lasted for about five or ten minutes more and then diffused into the perfectly blue sky, not to be seen again.

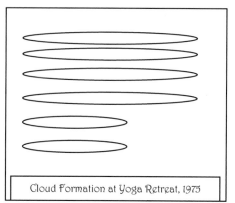

Cloud Formation at Yoga Retreat, 1975

Upon returning to my hometown of Buffalo NY, I went to a local bookstore and grabbed a copy of the Wilhelm Baynes edition of *The I Ching*, on the outside chance that a set of six parallel lines with four solid lines on top and two shorter lines on the bottom would be in the book. As I stumbled upon the Tun hexagram, with the bottom two lines having a space in the middle, I realized this was the closest one to the pattern in the sky that we witnessed. The Tun hexagram is named "Retreat" and one of the sayings in that section states, "Those who take time to retreat will obtain success later." This struck me very deeply, especially since I had also been studying the analytical psychology of Dr. Carl Jung, who teaches the principle of "synchronicity" where nature coincides with uniquely timed events to certain mental states of the observer.

After that experience, I can say that my life had changed in a fundamental way, with me wondering why I was one of the few who had noticed the cloud formation and why I didn't call attention to it for everyone's benefit and what it could mean in the larger context of my life direction. However, since Amrit Desai encouraged everyone to read the *Autobiography of a Yogi* throughout the yoga retreat, I decided to buy that book by Paramahansa Yogananda and start reading it.

A year later, at a Ram Dass weekend yoga retreat, I was asked during a confrontation with one of the leaders, "Who is your guru?" to which I answered, "Paramahansa Yogananda" which felt completely true to me. The person was quite surprised and asked, "Are you sure?" and I said, "Yes". Within an hour, I had packed up my belongings, collapsed my tent, and left with a triumphant feeling that I had made an inner discovery that subsequently provoked me to apply for the Meditation Lessons from Self-Realization Fellowship (SRF).

I encourage everyone interested in more detailed training than this introductory book provides to apply for the same lessons that started me on an inner growth experience, back in 1975, which continues to this day. The SRF Lessons are the most affordable and comprehensive correspondence course on yoga and meditation that is available today.

Thomas Valone
Wsshington DC

Chapter 1

Optimal Cognitive Function

*T*he practice of meditation can begin with just an attempt to try it once in a while. I guarantee that you will start to discover that it is the only time during the day where you might have no thoughts at all for a few moments AND receive ideas that help solve your most difficult problems. Of course, while the first few sessions may be rosy and very peaceful, you will also most likely go through a compensation experience that meditators call "dumping" where the unconscious finds an open door for that moment and dumps the emotional baggage that we all carry, back on the ego. However, the wonderfully encouraging "light at the end of the tunnel" is that this dumping will not last for very long, especially if you are diligent in a daily routine of meditation. The next image serves as a reminder of this "delayed gratification" benefit. Staying on the bridge by daily practice leads us toward the sunshine of all of the benefits outlined in this book. The reason is simple: there is much more good

Fig. 1 – Time, Aug. 6, 2003

to come of the experience than all of the emotional stuff that initially gets released. Everyone who practices meditation will attest to this simple discovery. Furthermore, meditation gets "deeper" as the years go by. While this phrase is a subjective descriptive, seasoned meditators have been scientifically correlated to a number of health and longevity benefits.

A daily practice for millions of people around the world, akin to prayer, meditation is now welcome in many health professional areas such as *psychoneuroimmunology* that have proven its efficacy. Medical doctors like D. S. Khalsa, author of *Brain Longevity*, say that meditation produces "optimal cognitive function" and have found that it is

9

positively rejuvenating for the brain and physiologically harmonizing for the body. In his book, Dr. Khalsa states that meditation causes:

A Decrease In:	An Increase In:
Oxygen consumption	Healthspan
Blood lactate	Lifespan
Heart rate	Hearing
Blood pressure	Vision
Respiration rate	Youthfulness
Cortisol production	Vitality

"A must-read for everyone interested in defending themselves against age-related loss of memory and other mental functions."
—ANDREW WEIL, M.D.

The Breakthrough Medical Program that Improves Your Mind and Memory

BRAIN LONGEVITY

Regenerate Your Concentration, Energy, and Learning Ability for a Lifetime of Peak Mental Performance

DHARMA SINGH KHALSA, M.D.
with Cameron Stauth

I personally was surprised to see vision and hearing listed but he is pretty emphatic, especially if you listen to the audiobook format. He also tells the story of teaching meditation to his medical students, who then scored the highest grades on the national test. He also teaches meditation to his patients. See Chapter 8 of this book for more information about his results.

This book is an outgrowth of my training seminars given to audiences at the U. S. Patent and Trademark Office, the American Cancer Society as well as the U. S. Psychotronics Association. It provides an introduction to the practice of modern meditation for Westerners, with added science and shortcuts.

People often like to know what will be covered, so here it is:

Meditation Training Summary

- - WHAT YOU WILL LEARN TODAY -
- Why should we practice daily meditation?
  - Scientific discoveries of meditation benefits
  - History of meditation in the U.S.
- Breathing Exercise #1
- Affirmation Exercise #2
- Visualization Exercise #3
- Exercise #4 - How to meditate daily

The subject of meditation applies to the mind. There is a wealth of research and developments that have a direct bearing on the effect of the mind over the body. Dr. Carl Simonton, author of *How to Meditate* and *Getting Well Again*, notes that a breakthrough was made in this area when *Nature* magazine published the finding that white blood cells have "neuroreceptors" on their surfaces. Thus, the physical connection between the mind and the immune system had been finally established. From the simplest example of pain control, which I have experienced, to the most extraordinary superhuman feats, it is concentration, visualization, and a meditative calm that achieves the

11

results. Recently in the dentist chair, Joyce the dental assistant said to me after a drilling without anesthetic, "I don't know how you do it. I've watched you and you are so calm. Some guys try to be macho and tense up. Do you study something to do that?" I said, "Yes, yoga and meditation practice."

When I was a teenager learning about meditation practices through Indra Devi's book *Yoga for Americans* (Prentice-Hall), I saw an oriental martial arts expert drill a hole into a solid brick with his finger. I was able to talk with him

afterwards and examine the brick as well. This was one of many feats that stuck in my mind as being physically difficult to explain.

At the U. S. Psychotronics Association's annual conference, I attended one of the "spoon-bending" parties with Jack Houck.[1] Years later, I also hosted one as well in my hometown,

Credit: Living Arts, www.gaiam.com

I witnessed more than one person bending the <u>bowl</u> of a tablespoon with two hands and in a few cases like with Jack himself, using their thumb as they held it in one hand! If I had not supplied the silverware myself for one of the parties and paid for Jack to host it in my hometown, I would have had some doubts. In one case, I sat right next to a young woman as she showed me how she did it (*make the suggestion and then wait for the softening, warming effect*). It still was amazing to me since I couldn't do it even with two hands and trying to cheat with a flat surface to push against! Everyone has heard of desperate mothers lifting an automobile off of their child in

---

[1] See www.JackHouck.com for articles of his about this phenomena.

an emergency. I have saved newspaper clippings of such events. All of the above examples show the extraordinary power of the mind over physical circumstances. An article on this subject by Jack Houck is featured in the anthology, *Energetic Processes: The Interconnection Between Matter, Energy, and Consciousness* by Moscow et al., (Xlibris Press.)

Chapter 2

History of Meditation in America

In this century, it wasn't until "for the first time in India's history a Swami was officially received by the President" that meditation became popular with Americans. The event was when Swami Yogananda, the founder of Self-Realization Fellowship, met President Calvin Coolidge at the White House, as reviewed on the front page of the *Washington Herald* (Jan. 25, 1927). That popularity was also evident when Yogananda subsequently filled Carnegie Hall to capacity, as well as many other lecture halls across the nation. Other meditation teachers also came before and after him: Swami Vivekananda, Meher Baba, and of course, Maharishi Mahesh Yogi who gave a new resurgence to meditation with a "transcendental" flair and attracted the Beatles and actress Mia Farrow back in the 1960's.

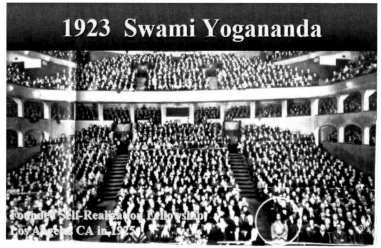

Yogananda was the first swami from India to come to the West to teach yoga. Packed auditoriums like Carnegie Hall

Today, Transcendental Meditation (or "TM") is probably the most familiar type of meditation known to Westerners, though Buddhist meditation is also very popular. Without meditation, Zen archers would miss their target. Without meditation, Qigong masters could not perform superhuman feats.

MAHARISHI

s the bearded, flower-decked, toga-clad Hindu monk who miles from the cover of LOOK magazine and East Village illboards. His disciples include the Beatles, Mia Farrow clerics, jazzmen, swingers and seekers. His message is ndividual joy and serenity and worldwide peace through TRANSCENDENTAL MEDITATION

This is the only book in which Maharishi describes the practices and techniques which have won him an international following.

lere, in his own words, are the methods which have led so

1963

The Science of Being and Art of Living by Maharishi Mahesh Yogi is published in London (US - 1968)

Leaving the Himalayas, Maharishi creates a international "Spiritual Regeneration Movement" with meditation centers in all major cities of the world, to establish joy, peace and serenity.

Seen here with the Beatles and also with Mia Farrow

Without meditation, Christian mystics would never have become saints. Without years of Transcendental Meditation practice, best-selling authors, Deepak Chopra, M.D. and John Gray, Ph.D. to name a few, would never have become famous. Even Dr. Andrew Weil was promoting meditation in a recent Time magazine article.

Today, there are now plenty of other not so famous people that also attribute their success to meditation. In the Appendix is an excellent article, also from Time magazine, that tells the story of a stock broker who says he has only survived the high pressure job, where all of his associates have moved on to positions elsewhere, by daily meditation.

Meditation

Dr. Andrew Weil practices daily meditation and recommends it for his patients. He practices what he preaches at his desert home near the University of Arizona at Tuscon.

The historical integration of yoga and meditation into modern Western society only took about fifty years to accomplish. Now, meditation is usually included at the end of most yoga classes across the country. It is offered daily as the most popular of many fitness classes at the US Patent Office. It is even taught at the US South Pole Station.

Today, meditation is so acceptable that a version called "mindfulness-based stress reduction" (MBSR) is becoming popular. The practice involves a moment-to-moment awareness and acceptance of one's thoughts, emotions, and physical sensations while seated in a meditation posture with the eyes closed. What is amazing with MBSR is that a six-month study conducted at the University of Maryland with 63 rheumatoid arthritis (RA) patients found a 35% reduction in psychological distress and an increased sense of well-being compared with the control group. As reported in a recent issue of *Arthritis Health Monitor* magazine (Feb/March, 2008), MBSR has been used for many years to help people to cope with stress, anxiety, chronic pain, headaches, stomach problems, sleep difficulties, fatigue, and high blood pressure. More information is available at www.umassmed.edu/cfm/mbsr . A psychotherapist with RA reports that, "If you are just present, there is a sense of peacefulness that makes everything better."

Once again, an ancient science has proven effective to provide modern remedies.

Articles from the Washington Herald, January, 1927 that I obtained from the Library of Congress

Chapter 3

Science Behind the Results

Meditation has so many wonderful benefits that rather than go through them one by one, I have prepared a table with the main results that you can expect, to summarize them.

Recent Research Results

1) Dramatic 23% reduction in death **from all causes**

2) Thickens **prefrontal cortex** thereby reversing the usual cortical thinning that occurs with age

3) Stimulates high frequency **gamma wave brain activity**

4) Lowers **blood pressure**, reduction in stress (lactate, cortisol) and the use of blood pressure medicine

5) Lowers **heart rate**, breathing rate and metabolism

6) Improves vision, hearing, youthfulness, **vitality**

(1) *Natural Health*, Nov. 2005, (2) *New Scientist*, Nov. 26, 2005, (3) *Wall Street Journal*, 11/5/2004, (4) *Diabetes Forecast*, Nov. 2005, (5) *British Med. J*, May 17, 2003, (6) *Brain Longevity*, Dr. Khalsa, 2001

Dr. Khalsa who was mentioned in Chapter 1, reports the surprising results of *improved vision and hearing* with regular meditation practice, besides an increase in youthfulness and vitality, which is quite impressive. However, to me the most significant findings for those of use passing the 50 mark is the thickening of the prefrontal cortex that normally thins with age. This lends great credence to the perceived increase in brain activity and harmonious, blissful experiences. Related to this is the stimulation of the highest vibrational brain frequencies that are known – gamma waves – in regular meditators.

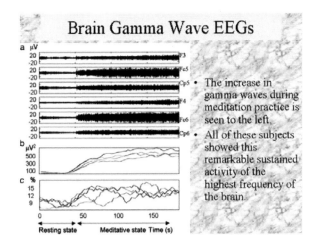

Brain Gamma Wave EEGs

- The increase in gamma waves during meditation practice is seen to the left.
- All of these subjects showed this remarkable sustained activity of the highest frequency of the brain.

See the *Neuroscience* journal article, reprinted in full in the Appendix, for all of the details on this meditation phenomenon.

Eastern philosophy and yoga, offer a viewpoint that the mind is more fundamental than matter. Demonstrating the power of meditation in consciously accomplishing physical abilities has been shown by the Menninger Foundation. Studies of Tibetan monks increasing their body

Results of laboratory tests done on the Yogi immediately before and after his 8 day stay in the pit.		
Investigation	Before	After
Body weight	55·0 kg.	50·5 kg.
Blood pressure	164/92 mm.	140/88 mm.
Pulse rate	106/min.	98/min.
Respiration rate	20/min.	16/min.
Oral temperature	37·2°C	34·8°C.
Blood sugar	88·0 mg. %	73·3 mg. %
Blood urea	30·0 mg. %	66·0 mg. %
Blood proteins	5·8 gm. %	5·5 gm. %
Blood calcium	9·8 mg. %	9·2 mg. %
Blood cholesterol	220·0 mg. %	300·0 mg. %
E.S.R. (Wintrobe)	1·5 mm.	18·0 mm.
Hemoglobin	12·5 g. %	12·0 g. %
Packed cell volume	34 %	39 %
Total leucocytes	4600/cmm	9200/cmm

temperature through the practice of "Tumo" or the *Indian Journal of Medical Research* articles (V. 49, 1, Jan. 1961, p.82) of yogis buried underground for extended periods of time are good examples. The article about the underground burial shows the electrocardiogram (ECG) records as the yogi's heart voluntarily stops and then, 8 days later, starts

19

Fig 2. The Yogi sitting in the pit while the ECG leads are being attached.

up an hour before the crypt is opened. They are fascinating accounts, very convincing and motivating to me.

More recently, a modern yogi, Sri Chinmoy, whom I have met before he recently passed away, had also amazed many researchers. Many people know of his music and involvement with sports figures. Sri Chinmoy also led peace meditations at the United Nations, U.S.

Record of Control of Heart and Pulse Rate by Meditation

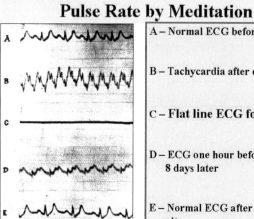

A	A – Normal ECG before entry
B	B – Tachycardia after entry in pit
C	C – Flat line ECG for 7 days
D	D – ECG one hour before opening 8 days later
E	E – Normal ECG after exit from pit

Congress, and at the British Parliment on a regular basis for years. However, not many may know of his extraordinary accomplishments in weight lifting. In two

20

separate witnessed and photographed events, with specially prepared equipment, Sri Chinmoy lifted 7,063 pounds dead weight with one hand and even more with two hands.

Sri Chinmoy

Famous for leading meditation and prayer at UN, inspiring sports and music stars to perform superhuman feats.

Sri Chinmoy lifts 7,063¾ pounds.

Using a specially designed weight machine, Sri Chinmoy lifted 7,063 pounds with one hand and even more with two hands.

He was not a muscle-bound person either. So how did he do it? Through meditation, one can convince the brain, or more scientifically, program our "biocomputer" to believe something is possible, with practice. The motivational speaker Anthony Robbins, author of *Unlimited Power*, tells us that it's only our beliefs that are holding us back and changing them is a technique that can be learned. Robbins is known for curing addictions in one session and training sharpshooters for the military, both by changing their belief systems.

Today, more and more Eastern techniques are emerging which have an ancient history to them such as "Qigong" (chi-gong). It is related to the more well-known practice of Tai Chi and teaches one how to move the life energy "chi" or "prana" through the body. Recently, a medical doctor from mainland China named Dr. Yan Xin has trained and healed thousands of people throughout the world with qigong methods ("The Secrets and Benefits of Qigong" audiotape

21

from Amber Leaf Press). In 1991, when President Bush Sr. met Dr. Yan Xin, he called him "a contemporary sage". Very important is the "relaxed and quiescent" state to the practice that Dr. Xin speaks of. A nervous or restless mind is not compatible with Qigong. This is also true of meditation and so specific techniques are needed to apply meditation to the Western mind successfully.

Bernie Siegel, M.D.

Professor, Yale Univ. School of Medicine

"The physical benefits of meditation have recently been well documented by Western medical researchers…normalize blood pressure, pulse rate, and levels of stress hormones in the blood…changes in attitude…reduction in the overcompetitive Type A behavior that increases the risk of heart attack. **Meditation also raises the pain threshold and reduces one's biological age**…helping people live longer and better."

Love, Medicine and Miracles, NY, Harper and Row, 1986

It should be noted that the very popular **"The Secret"** CD by Rhonda Byrne has a quote from her on Disk #1 where she notes that everyone ("without exception") who she  interviewed for the book, movie and CD practices meditation daily. These are people who have applied *The Secret* in their daily lives to dramatically fulfill their grandest wishes by affirming and believing it is already fulfilled and then act accordingly. She recommends 3 to 10 minutes per day for meditation.

Chapter 4 – Exercise #1

Breathing to Relax

WHY DO WE MEDITATE?

"We meditate to find, to recover, to come back to something of ourselves we once dimly and unknowingly had and have lost without knowing what it was or where or when we lost it" says Dr. LeShan, author of *How to Meditate* (Bantam, 1975). A scientist at a conference once told him his opinion of meditation: **"It's like coming home."** This, in a nutshell, summarizes the essence of this mysterious fourth state of consciousness (waking, dreaming, and sleeping being the other three). Dr. LeShan also states,

> Essentially, meditation seems to produce a physiological state of deep relaxation coupled with a wakeful and highly alert mental state...quite opposite from the state brought about by anxiety or anger.

However, meditation is not an excuse to sleep while sitting up! When done properly, meditation provides deeper rest than deep sleep, according to research done at Maharishi International University. Meditation produces subtle rewards that increase over time and often-surprising insight in just a few minutes of practice. It creates a balance between your inner and outer world. It also contributes to greater self-acceptance and therefore, greater self-esteem when you begin to carry what the yogis call a "portable paradise" within you. Meditation helps us to live more consciously as well since our sensitivity and receptivity increases. Lastly, meditation contributes to the inner feeling of positive personal growth being created day after day, as if we are continually evolving each time we meditate. Some believe that meditation actually helps us evolve.

23

The bubble diagram of TM, from the book *The Science of Being and the Art of Living* by Maharishi Mahesh Yogi (Signet, 1963), shows one tracing the thought of a mantra (a repeated word or sound) back to its source deep <u>below the normal level of consciousness</u>. This diagram helps us understand that *all of our restless thoughts are on the surface of our "level" of consciousness (A)*. As we meditate, we follow a "mantra" thought below the surface to create a new, deeper, more profound experience at level Z.

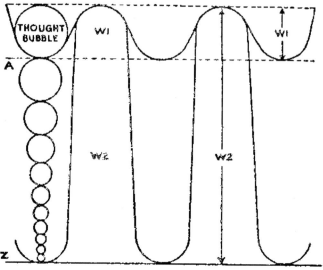

THE MAIN PRINCIPLE OF TRANSCENDENTAL DEEP MEDITATION

The bubble of thought rising from the level Z becomes bigger (*see illustration*). By the time it reaches the surface level A, it has developed enough to be appreciated as a thought. This is the level of the conscious mind.

BREATHING EXERCISE

Everyone takes breathing for granted, as part of the sympathetic nervous system, so much so that it remains mostly unconscious. In yoga, we strive to gain conscious control over the breath as a means to gain control over our states of consciousness.

Does anyone believe that we can change your consciousness and induce a relaxation response in less than 2 minutes? Read on and find out how.

Do this first exercise as the first stage of meditation practice. It will induce a tranquil, relaxation response (guaranteed!) and make it so much easier to enter a meditative state of consciousness more quickly.

It is called a "Ten-Ten-Ten Breathing Exercise" which makes breathing conscious. Sit with spine straight, preferably away from the back of the chair with the eyes closed:

1) Inhale slowly for the count of 10,
2) Hold for a count of 10 and look upward toward your inner visual screen with the eyes closed.
3) Then, slowly exhale for a count of 10.
4) Repeat a few times.

Exercise #1 10-10-10 BREATHING
Oxygenating Conscious
Control of Breath

INHALE deeply	HOLD & LOOK UP	EXHALE slowly
To a Count of 10	To a Count of 10	To a Count of 10

Doing this pranayama exercise, which moves "prana" or life energy, before meditating will:

(a) quickly interrupt the internal dialogue,
(b) improve the depth of meditation, and
(c) produce better and more satisfying results in a shorter period of time.

Doing just <u>one</u> of these 10-10-10 breaths is also what I call **"speed meditation"** and <u>can be done anywhere</u> to increase your concentration power immediately, <u>even in a car.</u> Yoga teaches that breath is the cord that ties the soul to the body. Practicing even this simple pranayama will lead one to having more influence over the autonomic nervous system activity, including the natural change in breathing during meditation, called the **"quieting of the breath in deep meditation,"** so it is imperceptible. This in turn will aid dramatically toward creating a deeply peaceful state of conscious awareness during meditation. Physiologically, the experience of restfulness for the advanced meditator has been found to be "deeper than deep sleep". I sometimes substitute an hour of meditation in the middle of the night for an hour of sleep to take advantage of such benefits.

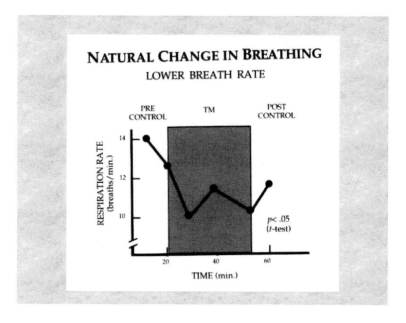

NATURAL CHANGE IN BREATHING
LOWER BREATH RATE

Chapter 5

Electrophysiology of Meditation

WHAT CAN WE EXPECT FROM MEDITATION?

Research psychologist, Dr. Lawrence LeShan, who I met years ago, says in his book, *How to Meditate* (Bantam Books):

> Central to the response to meditation is the lowered rate of metabolism, the lowered rate of using oxygen and producing carbon dioxide. That these decreases are due to a lowered metabolic rate rather than to a slower or shallower breathing is shown by the fact that both decrease equally and the ratio between them remains the same. This would not be true if it were due to alterations in respiration. There is also typically, in meditation, a slowing of the heartbeat...The lactate concentration of the blood decreases sharply during mediation, <u>nearly four times as fast as it does in people resting quietly</u>...the skin's electrical resistance increases sometimes as much as four hundred percent.

Thus, meditators show a profound lack of tension and anxiety, accompanied by an increase of slow alpha waves of the brain. Meditation can be scientifically described as a means for the brain to <u>electrically resonate</u>. As proven by EEG recordings, the practice bathes the brain in the harmonic frequencies most conducive to homeostasis (alpha and theta) that becomes pleasurable the longer you meditate. Compared to the usual "electrically noisy" waking state of the brain, meditation increases the "signal-to-noise" ratio as well. One study that I reviewed, performed by

27

scientists from Maharishi International University, showed the strong alpha and theta waves of the brain dominating the neuronal EEG patterns in a "waterfall" frequency plot over

Mobilization of the Latent Reserves of the Brain
THROUGH THE TRANSCENDENTAL MEDITATION TECHNIQUE

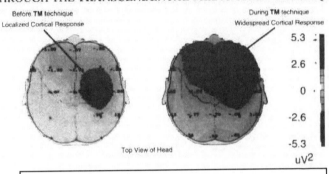

An increase in cortical response measured after TM practice

time. This study of the resonant modes of the brain drew the analogy of a **laser** cavity tuned to one major coherent frequency. As one stills the random, restless thoughts, meditation convinces the practitioner that he/she can be fully conscious and even blissful, without thinking thoughts. We then start to learn the profound truth taught by yogis that "we are not the mind." A single thought or word, such as a carefully chosen mantra (see next chapter), is the main vehicle to practicing meditation successfully

Meditation also increases the awareness of the self that is apart from the ego. Sometimes referred to as "self-actualization," **self-realization** has also been taught by many great philosophers like Hegel, Bradley, and Green as the "realization of the true self." It's a gradual process of connectedness that makes one feel more centered, aware of a larger Self and a necessary part of the universe.

28

Meditation tends to remarkably "expand consciousness" which can be accelerated with visualization exercises. The **expansion of consciousness** is difficult to describe in Western terms but the experience is breathtaking when it happens to the meditator. (See Chapter 7 for a specific visual aid.) Here "teaching by analogy" works best for the uninitiated—Swami Sri Yukteswar once said, "The little fishes of ideas make quite a stir in shallow minds while the whales of inspiration make hardly a ruffle in oceanic minds." This gives you an idea of how less perturbed one becomes when patience improves and calmness is a daily, learned habit. Another benefit is that one's **intuition improves**, which was amazing to me since my intuition was practically dead as a twenty-year old. I thought only women had the gift of intuition. Ideas which are accurate but *seem to come from nowhere,* as well as synchronicities, start occurring with more regularity as one perseveres with daily meditation practice. Meditation had other important benefits in my life too, such as relieving nervousness and even a tendency to stutter under stress, as I turned twenty-one.

Another arena of research that most people have never heard of is from the *American Journal of Cardiology.* I visited the Institute for Heart Math that conducted a test of the heart electrocardiogram (ECG) spectrum during different meditative states with a conscious intent. It was fascinating to me to see the results of a normal, incoherent ECG spectrum, compared with the very coherent and resonant ECG spectrum of a test subject with deep **appreciation** intent. Which heart rhythm would you rather have? The Institute teaches the concept of the heart as an intelligent organ. This research shows a surprising insight into the heart's complex processing ability which is much more expressive than its usual image of being simply a pump. The Heart Math Institute's published work shows conscious effects on the autonomic nervous system.

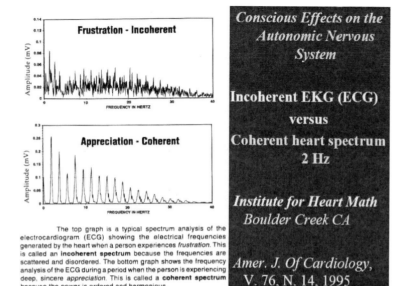

The top graph is a typical spectrum analysis of the electrocardiogram (ECG) showing the electrical frequencies generated by the heart when a person experiences *frustration*. This is called an **Incoherent spectrum** because the frequencies are scattered and disordered. The bottom graph shows the frequency analysis of the ECG during a period when the person is experiencing deep, sincere *appreciation*. This is called a **coherent spectrum** because the power is ordered and harmonious.

Conscious Effects on the Autonomic Nervous System

Incoherent EKG (ECG) versus Coherent heart spectrum 2 Hz

Institute for Heart Math Boulder Creek CA

Amer. J. Of Cardiology, V. 76, N. 14, 1995

ELECTRONIC MEDITATION

Some people believe that learning meditation is not necessary since there are many machines, many of which are patented, that put the brain in a state of meditation. Examples are James Gall's "Method and System for Altering Consciousness" Patent #5,123,899, also Robert Monroe's Patent 5,356,368 of almost the same title, and Tye Rubins' "Brain Wave Synchronizer" Patent #5,409,445. These were referred to as "electronic drugs" about ten years ago when they became very popular. I have tried a few of them, especially the ones with blinking lights in front of the eyes and low frequency tones for the ears. Though your brain may be driven to produce theta waves, your awareness can actually fight the experience since it may seem unexpected and often intrusive. They may work for some people but they don't allow the deep awareness to emerge from within which takes practice and bodily relaxation as well. Electronic drugs also can produce a dependency and a limit to the depth and scope of the experience. Therefore, I don't recommend them as a shortcut.

Chapter 6 – Exercise #2

Positive Affirmation

This chapter is the second key to successful meditation ability (the first was a breathing exercise). In the Buddhist tradition, the emptying of the mind is the key concept for meditation. Often a mandala or "yantra" is used to focus the mind to an interiorized state. In a *Time* article on Buddhism (10/13/97), the magazine says that enlightenment is regarded as the "awakening to the true nature of reality" but also, "a little below Nirvana." In the Hindu tradition, the final state of Samadhi is equivalent to Nirvana, but enlightenment is definitely regarded as the highest goal. To reach this goal, the ancient eight-fold path of Patanjali's *Yoga Sutras* is the accepted roadmap for the path of yoga taught in the schools of Raja Yoga, Kundalini Yoga, Kriya Yoga, etc.

The *Science of Yoga* by Taimni (Theosophical Press – available on Amazon.com), is probably the best translation, with excellent commentary that actually is scientific (Taimni was a biochemist) and is highly recommended. Patanjali's eight stages, which are expanded upon in the *Yoga Sutras*, consist of:

1) Self-restraint (Yama),
2) Observance (Niyama),
3) Posture (Asana),
4) Control of breath (Pranayama),
5) Withdrawl from sense perception (Pratyahara),
6) Concentration (Dharana),
7) Meditation (Dhyana),
8) Super-consciousness (Samadhi).

It can be said that the connection between meditation and religion is obvious. In a recent survey, respondents who used meditative prayer were twice as likely to feel a "strong

relationship with God" than if they stuck to the usual petitionary style of prayer. When we reflect that the word "religion" comes from the Latin "religio" meaning "to link back," it reminds us of Dr. LeShan's statements about "coming home," in regards to meditation.[2] Thus, meditation is inherently compatible with any religion, though it is often taught and practiced without any religious connotation. **The practice of meditation is effective, even if regarded simply as a technique.** Many

---

[2] The root of *religio* is from *religare* with the etymology "to bind back" in Funk & Wagnalls' *Standard College Dictionary* (1963 ed.). Similarly, "to link back" and "to reconnect" are found in Dr. Carl Jung's *Psychology and Religion: West and East* (2nd ed.), who also indicates that the latter definitions "originated with the Church Fathers" (p. 596).

people just meditate for what Dr. Herbert Benson called "the relaxation response" in his book with the same title. The main reasons professionals have for prescribing meditation for their patients are for <u>stress reduction</u> as well as <u>improving health</u> and <u>mental clarity</u>.

THE POWER OF AFFIRMATION

Another area of great help to meditators is the science of affirmation. Affirmations are really like guided meditations and a good introduction to the mental interiorization necessary for meditation. They work in conjunction with your goals. Furthermore, they have been shown to program your subconscious "biocomputer" with new habits and produce healthful results. Another less well known result are the **beneficial synchronistic events** from affirmation practice, such as the <u>first insight</u> in the book, *The Celestine Prophecy*, by James Redfield (Warner Books). As mentioned earlier, the effect of the concentrated conscious mind over objective reality usually surpasses normal expectations. **Affirmation practice is the key to creating major changes in one's life.** What we strongly believe usually becomes true for us, whether good or bad. Therefore, be careful, as

Anthony Robbins warns, of negative affirmations said during periods of anger or fear, such as "How could I be so stupid?" or "What if something bad happens?" for the mind will diligently try to answer every question posed by the ego. Instead, wise men suggest creating new, beneficial beliefs slightly beyond your comfort zone, repeat them mentally and see what positive things begin to happen. With the directions from his wonderful pocketbook, *Scientific Healing Affirmations*, Yogananda instructs us to:

Free the mind from restlessness and worries. Choose your affirmation and repeat all of it, first loudly, then softly and more slowly, until your voice becomes a

33

whisper. Then gradually affirm it mentally only...until you feel that you have attained a deep, unbroken concentration—not unconsciousness, but a profound continuity of uninterrupted thought.

The Power of Positive Thinking
Affirmation, Visualization, Meditation and Prayer
Dr. Norman Vincent Peale,
Published in 1952

The Power of Intention
Affirmation, Visualization, Meditation and Prayer
Dr. Wayne Dyer,
Published in 2004

Best selling books, 50 years apart, with timeless concepts

Once background mental repetition in a rhythmic fashion is achieved, **the affirmation takes on a life of its own** and we notice that it sort of "echos" in the mind as it keeps repeating (similar to a popular song after being heard). However, with its hidden power, days or weeks later, we find a change has taken place in our lives, which is beneficial and sometimes surprising. This is how the yogis change physical reality. Try one of these examples from the book,

"There is a hidden strength within me to overcome all obstacles and temptations",

"I am ever protected by omnipresent goodness,"

"I will purify my mind with the thought that God is guiding my every activity," or the one that I use very often,
"I will go forth in perfect faith in the power of omnipresent good to bring me what I need at the time that I need it."

34

Read it out loud a few times until it is memorized and then repeat mentally over and over as you release it. Other affirmations that I use often are: *"By sending goodwill to others, I will open a channel for God's love to come to me"* or my favorite, *"I am immersed in eternal Light. It permeates every particle of my being. I am living in that Light. The divine Spirit fills me within and without."* Memorize a few of them, like these that Yogananda says he has "spiritualized," to have a fully equipped weapon arsenal with you at all times, to use as needed on a moment's notice, especially for emergencies! **Thoughts are things.** Concentrated affirmation practice will prove it to you.

Below is a slide with many common affirmations to choose from. The one that asks the question, "Who is trying to still the mind?" comes from a 1939 book by Dr. Paul Brunton, *Discover Yourself* (Samuel Weiser, reprinted 1987), who suggests other affirmations like "Who am I?" and "Where is the origin of thoughts?" all designed to provoke an answer.

Exercise #2 Affirmation (mantra)

REPEAT ONE OF THESE THREE (3) TIMES OR MORE TO MEMORIZE

- Aum…Om…Peace…Relax…One…God…Tranquility
- **"I am ever-protected by Omnipresent goodness"**
- "I relax and cast aside all mental burdens"
- "The Lord is my Shepard"
- **"I am safe, calm, and protected"**
- "God is guiding my every activity"
- **"My cells absorb health and vitality from light"**
- "As I radiate goodwill to others, love will come to me"
- **"Who is it that is trying to make the mind still?"**

Brunton cautions, "When the beginner sits down to meditate, he is still largely held back by all sorts of strong worldly

35

feelings and thoughts" and so he advises that one should reduce the number of thoughts in order to succeed in meditation. Paul wrote many amazing books like *Search in Secret India,* which I highly recommend, that tell actual experiences and miracles that he witnessed while being in the presence of advanced yogis.

Choosing an affirmation, also called a 'mantra', for meditation helps the mind tremendously to overcome distractions during meditation. Returning to the affirmation after any distraction or spurious thought actively engages the mind and trains it to be "one-pointed" which also improves concentration ability. After a short period, one notices the benefits of **peacefulness,** a feeling of **joy,** or even a feeling of **love,** besides an inspiration that helps solve one's immediate problems.

Do not discount any of the four exercises in this book as trivial. Each one can be practiced independently and builds on the next to that the final modern meditation practice will be powerfully effective in your life!

INSURANCE FOR MEDITATION

Popular magazines like the *Washingtonian, Self, Time, SPA,* and *Let's Live,* have all had articles on meditation and yoga, with experts like Dr. Andrew Weil suggesting that inducing a state in which you are relaxed and emotionally comforted can have substantial health benefits. Insurance benefits are also available if you are a veteran or working at IBM or GM. The Veterans Administration, IBM, and GM all pay for part of Transcendental Meditation training under the category of "stress management."

36

Chapter 7 – Exercise #3

Visualization

"Half an hour's meditation each day is essential, except
when you are busy. Then a full hour is needed."
                                            - St. Francis de Sales

As we enter the third and last exercise before combining
them all into one meditation practice, it is good to reflect
upon the value of this training as expressed by St. Francis
de Sales. While the world demands attention and time from
us, we will find that giving a short period to meditation each
day increases our efficiency and effortlessness during
performance of our work. Some of the reasons for this are
cited in the TM ad below.

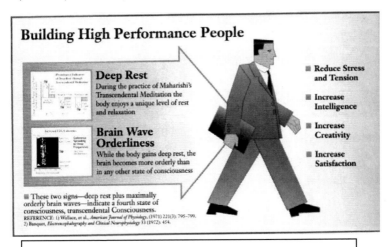

Building High Performance People

Deep Rest
During the practice of Maharishi's
Transcendental Meditation the
body enjoys a unique level of rest
and relaxation

Brain Wave Orderliness
While the body gains deep rest, the
brain becomes more orderly than
in any other state of consciousness

- Reduce Stress and Tension
- Increase Intelligence
- Increase Creativity
- Increase Satisfaction

These two signs—deep rest plus maximally
orderly brain waves—indicate a fourth state of
consciousness, transcendental Consciousness.
REFERENCE: 1) Wallace, et al., *American Journal of Physiology*, (1971) 221(3): 795–799.
2) Banquet, *Electroencephalography and Clinical Neurophysiology* 33 (1972): 454.

Transcendental Meditation Promotional Ad

One of the best visual symbols that I feel is very powerful for the human evolution is the **plant, flower, or tree.** All three of these plant kingdom species can teach us a lot. They reach toward the light and pull in sustenance from their outstretched limbs, as well as from their roots. Therefore,

this book has the tree as its symbolic meditation process. In the Modern Meditation workshop that I lead, I like to have the participants stand up, inhale deeply and extend their hands to reach for the sky and the stars and **mentally try to become one with the universe.** Then, as we sit to meditate, the best visualization is to have the brain cells at the top of

the cortex all reach out just as the hands and arms did during the practice to become one with everything in the universe. Remember what the Buddhist monk said to the hot

Wheels of Life – A. Judith

dog salesman? "Make me one with everything." This is how the proverbial "thousand petal lotus" at the crown charka works to open up and create a "cosmic consciousness" experience for you. It just needs an intention, visualization and emotion to make it happen, along with daily repetition. Simmer for several years and presto, your consciousness will have changed permanently! The physical basis for this

visualization practice can be found in the book, *The Non-Local Universe* by Robert Nadeau (Oxford, 1999) where physicist Nadeau explains **quantum entanglement.** He notes the long distance experiments between entangled photons "obliged physicists to conclude that nonlocality or non-separability is a global or universal dynamic of the life of the cosmos." Thus we can also conclude that our body's atoms are also non-separable from the universe, so it is good to visualize this.

We should learn how to visualize our thoughts—how to recharge them with the energy of concentration until they become visible manifestations.
—Paramahansa Yogananda

From SRF *Inner Reflections* engagement calendar

The **practice of looking upward** with the eyes closed also tends to draw the consciousness upwards, which can easily be physically perceived during meditation. Picture the artistic drawing from the *Wheels of Life* book on the previous page and know that you are drawing all of your nervous and conscious energy <u>upwards</u> to the cerebral region. By letting your gaze drop downwards during meditation, you will invariably go into a sleep state, which is adverse to meditation and makes one more unconscious. Make sure you have enough rest first or enough concentration ability so that sleep will not become any part of your meditation. This is very important because habits are strong and I have seen weekly meditators at group meditations who are recognizable because their heads are down against their chest during meditation. We can only hope they will eventually look up while meditating.

Another additional aid in getting the spinal energy of kundalini to help your meditation is to **visualize a white vertical tube for the spine,** lit up like a fluorescent bulb, has helped me focus on "retreating to the spine and brain", which is a powerful but advanced technique.

Visualize your Human Body as a Tree or a Flower

An additional suggestion is that it is very helpful to visualize a **small white, glowing ball of energy** ascending from your *muladara chakra*, at the perineum "base of the spine" upwards to rest at the point between the eyebrows and even to the top of the head. In deep meditations, this visualization aids in making one detach from the consciousness of the body. It starts to happen slowly as time goes on, starting from the lower part of the body and moving upwards, until it seems that only the spine and brain are present in your field of awareness. That is when the mental space of meditation, or "the darkness behind closed eyes" begins to expand and "lighten."

Not sure what a *muladara chakra* is? Next time you are in a tall building or bridge high above the ground, look down over the edge or out the window. If it is done suddenly, you will feel a strong sensation of survival and vertigo kicking in from the perineum that also awakens your adrenaline.

Exercise #3 Visualization

- **Bring Energy Up – like Qi Gong**
- **"Prayerize, Visualize, Actualize" – Dr. Norman Vincent Peale**
- **Visualize the fulfillment of your desire as if it has already occurred – Dr. Wayne Dyer**
- **Use visualization to counter disease, strengthen immune system and create conscious safety, calmness, protection, health and vitality – Dr. Carl Simonton**
- **Visualize the spine as a trunk of a tree and your brain as the branches with the top of your head as the leaves reaching toward the sun**
- **Expansion into infinity visualization – advanced practice**

What a *kundalini awakening* or the state of *samadhi* may feel like can be imagined by mentally visualizing an **expanding bubble of consciousness** from the room to the building, city, country, world, solar system, galaxy, and finally letting go to infinity to mentally touch the universe, while you add as much intense joy as possible. This is also a good visualization to use at the start of meditation. Another similarly fulfilling visualization taught by Yogananda in the pocket book, *Metaphysical Meditations,* is to deliberately **increase the feeling of joy** as a growing bubble, expanding it to infinite size whenever we find ourselves feeling happy. This also works well to start a meditation session since you will then be meditating on joy!

41

Chapter 8

Is Meditation Powerful Enough?

SOME SUGGESTIONS

In the beginning of meditation practice, the most important task you can accomplish, which may take all of your will power and determination, is to <u>sit still</u>, in silence, for at least 10 minutes each day. If you can promise yourself or someone else, that you will keep such a commitment to create this beneficial habit, it will become your resource. *Yoga Journal* once stated, "The more trouble you have allocating twenty minutes a day for meditation, the more desperately you probably need it." Having your own "meditation room" in the house is a great reinforcement for the importance of this practice. I was also happy to see that BWI Airport in Baltimore MD has a meditation room. Going to a weekly meditation group, such as an **Employee Sponsored Meditation Group** (like the Pentagon has maintained for over twenty years), can become an oasis of peacefulness and restoration in an otherwise hectic week.

At first, the subconscious mind tends to use the time to "dump" on you. All of your worries, troubles, desires, etc. will at first plague many or most of your meditations. A lot of people get discouraged at this point if day after day it seems that they are not really meditating. However, that is a trap created by the ego. Instead, this experience of "clearing" the mind of "garbage thoughts," as meditators call them, is *very therapeutic*. It makes way for the clear inspirations to come and the "space between thoughts" which becomes blissful. By the way, **"bliss"** is the Eastern phrase for the very subtle joy that wells up from deep within everyone who becomes proficient at meditation. It is so peaceful, transforming and expansive that meditators sometimes call it **"transcending"** because in reality, it is like a new level of consciousness. Often it lasts for a while after meditation period is over, even up to a week if you meditate for a longer time. More so, it is directly proportional to the <u>length and depth</u> of meditation. In other words, if you meditate for an hour or so but not very deeply, another "deeper" meditation may be more refreshing and have lasting effects, though it is shorter.

I have experienced transforming and memorable changes in longer meditations that in some cases have become milestones for me in my spiritual evolution. I've had three-hour meditations at home where the last hour is the most exciting and uplifting. The inspirations that come make it all worthwhile and memorable, especially when combined with prayer. St. Teresa of Avila, for example, called meditation the **"prayer of quiet"** for good reason (*The Interior Castle*, Doubleday). I've also participated in 6 and 8-hour meditations with our DC Meditation Center in College Park, Maryland. To reassure those who can't imagine such a long time "doing nothing," the first thing one invariably finds is that the time passes quickly for an experienced meditator who does not have a lot of mental noise. It is the mental distractions that create the awareness of time. Meditators benefit from longer meditations, especially if they mentally prepare for the experience by "cleaning house" first.

Mentally retreating to the spine and brain helps this process. Often referred to in yoga as "kundalini," the upraising of spinal energy and consciousness is central to the universal phenomena of meditation. In fact, Gopi Krishna, author of *The Biological Basis of Religion and Genius*, and also Dr. Lee Sanella, author of *Kundalini: Psychosis or Transcendence?* both believe that the kundalini process is biologically inherent in all human beings. Sometimes the mental expansion it induces happen spontaneously, as in the case with Gopi Krishna, following years of daily meditation.

Is Meditation Powerful Enough?

"Occasionally my patients will add various elements of their brain longevity programs one at a time, and will **delay** their participation in meditation. Sometimes they put off meditation for a week or two, because it **seems exotic** to them, particularly if they are older patients who have never meditated. But when they do finally begin to meditate, they *invariably* report to me that the meditation 'took them to a new level.' Meditation is really that powerful." D.S. Khalsa MD, *Brain Longevity*, 1997

Sleep Replacement - Red Eye plane trip story
Insomnia solution – Sit up and meditate - Valone

CENTERS OF CONSCIOUSNESS

Looking up while your eyes are closed activates the **frontal lobe of the brain**, which provides our advanced insights and our sense of inspiration if activated properly. By looking downward, one will start to feel sleepy, even while sitting up. Another finding is that the concept of "higher consciousness," like higher vibration levels, is a physical phenomenon as well. What we focus upon with concentration, we often can bring into being. Therefore, by concentrating upwards with our eyes closed during meditation, we can awaken the frontal lobe and what the Eastern mystics call "the spiritual eye" (Ajna center), the tunnel of light, as well as the highest "crown chakra" center of consciousness, (Sahasrara) at the top of the head. Recall that many paintings of saints show a "halo" around the top of the head because the crown chakra has opened in that saint which covers the entire crown or top of the head. Research has also shown that **long-term meditators** (those with 15 years experience) **have thicker frontal lobes** than nonmeditators (*Time*, Feb. 23, 2009, p. 64).

44

HOW IT WORKS

EASTERN VIEW   WESTERN VIEW

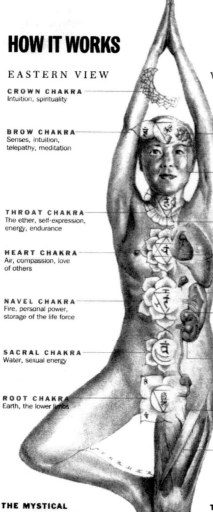

CROWN CHAKRA
Intuition, spirituality

BROW CHAKRA
Senses, intuition,
telepathy, meditation

BRAIN
Triggers relaxation
response

PITUITARY GLAND
May signal glands to
secrete fewer stress
hormones

THROAT CHAKRA
The ether, self-expression,
energy, endurance

THYROID GLAND
May signal glands
to secrete fewer
metabolic hormones

HEART CHAKRA
Air, compassion, love
of others

HEART
Strengthens circulatory
system, lowers blood
pressure

LUNGS
Improves deep breathing

NAVEL CHAKRA
Fire, personal power,
storage of the life force

**ADRENAL
GLANDS**
May deactivate stress
response by
suppressing adrenalin

SACRAL CHAKRA
Water, sexual energy

KIDNEYS
Enhances drainage
of waste from lymphatic
system

ROOT CHAKRA
Earth, the lower limbs

**REPRODUCTIVE
ORGANS**
May influence secretion
of sex hormones

MUSCULATURE
May improve muscle
tone and prevent injury

THE MYSTICAL
Enlightenment and good health
require the free flow of the life
force (**prana**) and the proper
balance between the seven
major energy hubs (**chakras**).
An eighth chakra, or aura,
surrounds the body and
encompasses the other seven.)
The three lower chakras serve
the body's physical needs,
while the five upper chakras
are associated with the spiritual
realm.

THE SCIENTIFIC
Breathing exercises have been
shown to decrease **blood
pressure** and lower levels of
stress hormones. Stretching
the body through various poses
promotes better drainage of
the **lymphatic vessels,** the
body's waste-removal system.
Holding postures may build
muscle tone, which enhances
physical well-being and pro-
tects delicate **joints** against
injury.

TIME magazine, 4-23-01, p.61

The practice of **looking upward with the eyes closed** also tends to draw the consciousness upwards, which can easily be physically perceived during meditation. Other chakras, as indicated in *Time* (4/23/01) include the throat center (Vishuddha) of powerful speech, the heart center (Anahata) where the feeling of love is the strongest, the lumbar center (Manipura) which is also called the power center of "chi" for martial arts, the sacral center (Svadhistana) of sex energy, and the root chakra (Muladhara) of survival at the perineum (most books simply say "the bottom of the spine"). I discovered my Muladhara chakra on June 15, 1977 quite unexpectedly while coincidentally in Chicago at the 2nd International Congress on Meditation and Related Therapies. I stuck my head out of a window from the 15th story of the YMCA to look down to the street. Try it sometime, from any tall building or bridge, looking down suddenly to the ground. The overwhelming, fearful surge of self-preservation radiating from the perineum is unforgettable. Otherwise, the Muladhara center is mostly dormant in civilized, daily life. For those interested in an interdisciplinary understanding of the nature of the chakras, Dr. Caroline Myss in the book, *Anatomy of the Spirit*, has proven a strong correlation exists between the 7 chakras, the 7 sacraments, and the 7 rungs of the Sefirot.

Not many people may know that the reality of the chakras of the body as centers of consciousness, has been shown by a UCLA professor, Dr. Valerie Hunt, who, during ten years of research, recorded electrode signal from the major body chakras during various states of consciousness. An example is shown here from *Wheels of Light* (Simon & Schuster) by aura reader, Rosalyn Bruyere, who worked closely with Dr. Hunt for all of those years. During her lectures, Dr. Hunt showed that new distinctive frequency spectra are measurable from these centers, apart from the EMG and EEG frequency ranges, correlating to predominant colors of the "aura." She is currently working

46

on an advanced biofeedback machine based upon her findings. (Dr. Hunt's lectures on DVD are available from the USPA where she spoke two years in a row.) Dr. Hunt's work is the first to prove that aura "colors" are objective, measurable states of consciousness, distinctly identifiable. Her work has profound implications for alternative health and wellness research. It could bring this esoteric subject of chakras and auras into the mainstream medical community, in the same way that acupuncture became accepted in the West, after research proved its worth.

Regarding the higher centers of consciousness normally activated during meditation, one indication that they are opening is the internal experience of light. Inexperienced meditators may laugh but remember that the pineal gland, esoterically connected to the crown chakra, *responds to light* though deep in the brain. This mystery of it being "optically activated" has been related to the reception of direct sunlight on the eyes. Esoterically, what I have found, especially during longer meditations, lasting a few hours, is

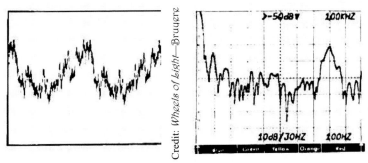

Violet chakra signal and its spectrum – Dr. Hunt

that it appears to the meditator that someone has "turned on the ceiling light" in the room. This may be a result of meditation directly stimulating the pineal gland. Other times, various deep colors will be seen on the internal mental screen. Most often, simply a white, opal glow will be perceived as one relaxes into a deep meditation.

SPEED MEDITATION: A QUICK SHORTCUT

Here is an example of a **consciousness changing breathing exercise** or *pranayama* which I discovered that helps in times of drowsiness, especially while driving or working long hours is the following. It is also very similar to one of the kundalini exercises taught in the book by Dr. Khalsa. This "Speed Meditation" will give you in a few seconds a close approximation to a regular meditation:

1) **Inhale** and draw energy up the spine and look up;
2) **Hold the breath** as you concentrate at the point between the eyebrows;
3) **Exhale** only after a minimum of 10 seconds. It only takes 10-15 seconds or so to feel the tingling sensation in the middle of the forehead and the expanding blood vessels in the brain, which will invariably awaken even a sleepy driver or a drowsy office worker.

Holding the breath has been proven to cause the brain's blood vessels to expand in compensation. This immediately improves brain circulation and alertness. Practicing this each day will also directly improve your mental faculties.

ANCIENT MEDITATION AND PRAYER

The *Man, Myth and Magic* encyclopedia (Marshall Cavendish, BPC Pub.) says that meditation was "once regarded almost exclusively as a preoccupation of mystics, saints and hermits." It goes on to say that the ancient Chinese practiced a Taoist form of meditation, trying to reduce all striving for a goal. In the Islamic mystical tradition, Sufis sit in solitude repeating the name of Allah without ceasing. Buddhist meditators will often use a mandala, an elaborate symmetrical, circular design representing the cosmos, to focus their attention. Jewish followers of the Kabbalah meditate on the treelike "sefiroth"

48

or the chariot "Merkabah" to carry their consciousness upwards.

Meditation has also been a practice of Christian contemplatives and mystics as well including St. Francis and St. Ignatius of Loyola. For example, St. Teresa of Avila is well known for her four-stage **"water wheel"** analogy (*The Way of Perfection*, Doubleday). At first it is a lot of work for the aspirant to pump the water of devotion to feed the garden of the soul. However, by the four stage, the water flows freely and unaided. In fact, **prayer, contemplation and meditation** are very closely related, as the cardiologist Dr. Larry Dossey has pointed out in his books, such as *Prayer is Good Medicine*. Dr. Dossey has also proven, through many articles now published in medical journals, that prayer can effect healing changes even in unsuspecting patients, most often in the range of 40% to 50% efficacy, which he points out is a huge percentage of patients, signifying a major effect beyond chance. (Dr. Dossey was the keynote speaker at the USPA Conference in 2001, so I was also able to meet him personally. I highly recommend the DVD of his lecture to everyone.)

Positive Therapeutic Effects of Intercessory Prayer in a Coronary Care Unit Population

RANDOLPH C. BYRD, MD, San Francisco, Calif

ABSTRACT: The therapeutic effects of intercessory prayer (IP) to the Judeo-Christian God, one of the oldest forms of therapy, has had little attention in the medical literature. To evaluate the effects of IP in a coronary care unit (CCU) population, a prospective

Southern Med. Journal, V. 81, No. 7, July, 1988, p. 826
"One of the best single-blind studies on prayer ever conducted," according to Dr. Larry Dossey – 7/01.

Many spiritual leaders of various religions go even further by teaching that anything is possible through prayer. What better state of mind for an effective prayer, clear of mental "noise and static," than just after meditation? In Yogananda's book, *How You Can Talk With God*, it says,

> "We should speak to the Divine Spirit with confidence and with a feeling of closeness, as to a father or a mother. Our relationship with God should be one of unconditional love."

God's response, he also states, can be felt during meditation "as peace, as love, or as joy." Meditation is referred to in the Biblical sayings, "Be still and know that I am God," "If thine eye be single, thy whole body shall be filled with light," and "The kingdom of God is within you." These sayings have great significance that can be explored during deep meditation by using them as a mantra. With three national studies all in agreement that 90% of Americans believe in God, the acknowledgement of God in our lives during meditation practice can improve one's spiritual growth and feeling of closeness to the Divine.

For me, the striving for stillness, even of the breath and heart, along with the concentrated focus of one-pointed devotion within the depths of meditation, after a prayer, have been very important tools, which have created memorable breakthroughs for me in meditation.

In the next chapter, we will combine the last three exercises into one to start you on your meditation journey of a lifetime. If you are not sure whether you can attain the status of a "highly spiritual" person, take heart. Research has shown that those who describe themselves as highly spiritual tend to exhibit an **asymmetry in the thalamus** of their brain. However, those who persevere through just eight weeks of training in meditation skills will **develop the same feature** (*Time*, Feb. 23, 2009, p. 64). Therefore, I invite all of my audiences and readers to take the **Eight-Week Challenge** to see the difference in their lives of doing **Exercise #4** in the next chapter each day for 8 weeks. Who knows, you might enjoy the multiple benefits so much that you decide to continue indefinitely.

Chapter 9 – Exercise #4

Modern Meditation Technique

MANTRA MEDITATION

Meditating "about" something is essentially contemplation, which Patanjali's YOGA SUTRAS define as "*Dhyana*," where the concentration (*Dharana*) is narrowed and focused to discern the foundational essence of the object of meditation. This process will naturally happen as we mentally concentrate on the repetition of an affirmation or mantra. To quote Evelyn Underhill from her 500-page treatise called *Mysticism* (Oneworld Pub.), written in 1911,

> The modern American schools of mental healing and New Thought recommend concentration upon a carefully selected word as the starting-point of efficacious meditation.

Examples that are popular today include Exercise #2 (Chapter 6) with the words such as, "one," "aum," "tranquility," "the Lord is my shepherd," or a direct command like "relax." One can also ask a single identity question, as Paul Brunton suggests in *Discover Yourself* (Samuel Weiser Pub.), with the question,

> **Who is it that is trying to make the mind still?** Then you must wait reverently. The answer will be heralded by an intuition, a gentle sense, and something very indeterminate. You cannot force it. You must pay the keenest attention and yield yourself up to it. That is the higher meditation, when you let the interior world reveal itself to you.

This carefully chosen line of questioning, from my experience, can create a *consciousness breakthrough* when used as a point of concentration with earnest sincerity.

To summarize, follow these three simple steps for your meditation practice. As a preliminary preparation, stretch forward, back, and side to side briefly if possible and then sit upright with the eyes closed, relaxing the body and calming the mind, while putting aside all outward thoughts, giving this time exclusively to meditation. You may also being with a prayer if you are so inclined to help elevate your consciousness and spiritualize the experience.

Exercise #4 Meditation

- **Sit upright with eyes closed.**
- **Do Breathing Exercise #1**
- **Relax from top of head to bottom of feet**
- **Do Affirmation Exercise #2**
- **Watch the breath as you repeat mantra**
- **Do Visualization Exercise #3**
- **If thoughts intrude, just say, "relax" and go back to your mantra of choice**

* * *

1)   Do the 10-10-10 breathing exercise from the previous section, (Exercise #1) thus gaining control over the breath.

2)   Pick a single word or phrase (mantra) which has meaning for you. In a similar fashion as affirmation practice, repeat the mantra in your mind, returning to the mantra when you get distracted (Exercise #2).

3)   Simply watch the breath, gently bringing the mind back to your single purpose, as you continue to relax and let go of every thought except one, adding a visualization to your meditation to give it even more dynamic power (Exercise #3).

* * *

Practice on a regular basis, for 10-15 minutes (Dr. Simonton suggests that we can also start with once-a-week, then twice-a-week, then finally daily.) Most meditators find daily practice well worth the effort. Suggestion: it is important while the habit is being formed, you practice regularly, with an empty stomach, even if only for five minutes, rather than skip the agreed-to routine because of some "emergency."

Visualizing a **white vertical tube for the spine**, lit up like a fluorescent bulb, has helped me focus on "retreating to the spine and brain", which is a powerful but advanced technique. Yogananda suggests that whenever you see a quiet pond without waves, stop and meditate nearby with eyes partly open, concentrating on quieting the mind to make it as calm as the pond. Merging and expanding one's awareness of light, peace, love, or joy, is the certainly the best course to take, while consciously feeling gratitude in one's heart. Then we can understand why the ancient BHAGAVAD GITA from India, says that meditation induces **"radiance of character."**

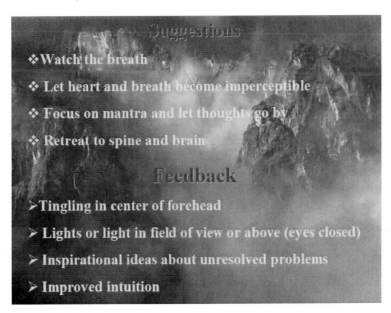

Suggestions

❖ Watch the breath
❖ Let heart and breath become imperceptible
❖ Focus on mantra and let thoughts go by
❖ Retreat to spine and brain

Feedback

➢ Tingling in center of forehead
➢ Lights or light in field of view or above (eyes closed)
➢ Inspirational ideas about unresolved problems
➢ Improved intuition

Chapter 10

Signs of Progress in Meditation

HATHA YOGA AND PRANAYAMA

A natural approach to relaxation and flexibility is Hatha Yoga stretching. Often a state of mind can only be optimized if the body is free from tension, pain and distraction. Yoga *asanas* or Hatha Yoga postures, offered at many fitness centers, can be very beneficial for toning and stretching the ligaments, muscles, and spine. I go to a yoga class once a week. Yoga teaches that maintaining a flexible spine ensures the flow of *kundalini* energy upwards during meditation. Furthermore, doing a *pranayama* exercise (moving prana energy with the breath and concentrated visualization) such as the fire breath, *khapalabhakta* breathing, or even the gentle Kriya Yoga technique, helps clear the spinal "blockages" which keep our attention at the lower chakras. The Kriya technique, for example, also enables the meditator to feel the spinal currents of energy and use them beneficially to enhance the meditation experience. Even the beginner's Hong Sau technique is also a powerful pranayama capable of quieting the breath and focusing the attention at the highest spiritual centers. Hatha yoga and pranayama are additional techniques that help prepare the body and mind for meditation.

PURIFICATION BY FASTING

After going through a difficult time, I attended my first 10-day yoga retreat by Yogi Amrit Desai at Ursinus College in 1975, fasted for three days on watermelon, and ate mostly live vegetarian food for the rest of the retreat. Near the end, some of us saw several clouds line up in the sky in a formation, as mentioned in the Preface, which I later found

54

to resemble the Tun hexagram from the I Ching, which is entitled "retreat." Along with the pranayama breathing exercises, this purifying yoga experience convinced me that consciousness can be favorably and profoundly changed without drugs. Furthermore, the saying that meditation practice improves intuition became abundantly clear to me afterwards, with several meaningful synchronicities starting to happen to me.

Fasting on fruit juice, for example, is something that my wife and I now do almost every week and recommend it as a purifying method for the body and brain. Books on fasting (such as *Fasting, the Super Diet* by Shirley Ross) describe how the body dumps toxins during a fast. My thinking and meditations become clearer during and after fasting, even if it is only done for one day.

CONCLUSION

Meditation today is proven to be physiologically transforming and recommended by doctors. To review, we have learned the practice of mantra meditation, where it is recommended to stick with one mantra you choose for at least a month or more before trying another one. We also practiced a powerful breathing exercise that helps awaken brain cells through oxygen therapy. I also included a "speed meditation" technique for those extra moments to help you get ahead. The discussion of kundalini and the chakras, vital to the advanced yogi, gave a basis for the deeper benefits that can be achieved through regular meditation. Also helpful in transforming the conscious mind is the astounding changes a person can experience through the correct practice of affirmation, implanted in the mind by concentrated repetition. Thus, as you progress in affirmation and meditation practice, you may rightly expect some or all of the following:

· An increasing peacefulness during meditation.

- A conscious inner experience of calmness in meditation metamorphosing into increasing bliss.
- A deepening of one's understanding, and finding answers to one's questions through the calm intuitive state of inner perception.
- An increasing mental and physical efficiency in one's daily life.
- Love for meditation and the desire to hold onto the peace and joy of the meditative state in preference to attraction to anything in the world.
- An expanding consciousness of loving all with the unconditional love that one feels toward his own dearest loved ones.
- Actual contact with God, and worshipping Him as ever-new bliss felt in meditation and in His omnipresent manifestations within and beyond all creation. -Yogananda (Self-Realization magazine, Spring, 1992)

You may choose to take meditation lessons locally from a yoga center or through more than one correspondence courses offering meditation instructions. Dr. Carl G. Jung, founder of analytical psychology, said that yoga and meditation promise "undreamed-of possibilities." This is also the title of a free introductory booklet available from Self-Realization Fellowship, (3880 San Rafael Ave., Los Angeles, CA 90065) describing excellent and inexpensive meditation lessons, including the Kriya and Hong Sau techniques. Meditate to improve alertness, mindfulness, general health and well-being, while enhancing one's spiritual practice, whatever that may be...or as Yogananda says, "Why not unite all your smaller lights, letting them shine forth in one splendid effulgence to illumine the bodily house in which you dwell?"

As you consider where to meditate, it is nice to have a meditation room set aside at home but any room will do. However, I have also used the Metro subway, office cubicle, and even the restroom stall when necessary. The benefits outweigh the awkwardness of the surroundings!

Signs of Progress in Meditation

- Peacefulness during and after meditation
- Joy and bliss as a peak experience
- Increasing mental and physical efficiency
- Occasional synchronicity
- Compassion for others
- Desire to meditate regularly and deeply
- Contact with the Divine

Where Can I Meditate?

- Meditation Room
- Bedroom
- Living Room
- Metro
- Office Cubicle
- Restroom Stall

Appendix

Reference Articles on Meditation

Meditation Gives Brain a Charge, Study Finds

Marc Kaufman, *Washington Post*, Jan 3, 2005, P. A05
http://www.washingtonpost.com/wp-dyn/articles/A43006-2005Jan2.html

Brain research is beginning to produce concrete evidence for something that Buddhist practitioners of meditation have maintained for centuries: Mental discipline and meditative practice can change the workings of the brain and allow people to achieve different levels of awareness.

Those transformed states have traditionally been understood in transcendent terms, as something outside the world of physical measurement and objective evaluation. But over the past few years, researchers at the University of Wisconsin working with Tibetan monks have been able to translate those mental experiences into the scientific language of <u>high-frequency gamma waves</u> and brain synchrony, or coordination. And they have pinpointed the left prefrontal cortex, an area just behind the left forehead, as the place where brain activity associated with meditation is especially intense.

"What we found is that the longtime practitioners showed brain activation on a scale we have never seen before," said Richard Davidson, a neuroscientist at the university's new $10 million W.M. Keck Laboratory for Functional Brain Imaging and Behavior. "Their mental practice is having an effect on the brain in the same way golf or tennis practice will enhance performance." It demonstrates, he said, that the brain is capable of being trained and physically modified in ways few people can imagine.

Scientists used to believe the opposite -- that connections among brain nerve cells were fixed early in life and did not change in adulthood. But that assumption was disproved over the past decade with the help of advances in brain imaging and other techniques, and in its place, scientists have embraced the concept of ongoing brain development and "neuroplasticity."

Davidson says his newest results from the meditation study,

published in the Proceedings of the National Academy of Sciences in November, take the concept of neuroplasticity a step further by showing that mental training through meditation (and presumably other disciplines) can itself change the inner workings and circuitry of the brain.

The new findings are the result of a long, if unlikely, collaboration between Davidson and Tibet's Dalai Lama, the world's best-known practitioner of Buddhism. The Dalai Lama first invited Davidson to his home in Dharamsala, India, in 1992 after learning about Davidson's innovative research into the neuroscience of emotions. The Tibetans have a centuries-old tradition of intensive meditation and, from the start, the Dalai Lama was interested in having Davidson scientifically explore the workings of his monks' meditating minds. Three years ago, the Dalai Lama spent two days visiting Davidson's lab.

The Dalai Lama ultimately dispatched eight of his most accomplished practitioners to Davidson's lab to have them hooked up for electroencephalograph (EEG) testing and brain scanning. The Buddhist practitioners in the experiment had undergone training in the Tibetan Nyingmapa and Kagyupa traditions of meditation for an estimated 10,000 to 50,000 hours, over time periods of 15 to 40 years. As a control, 10 student volunteers with no previous meditation experience were also tested after one week of training.

The monks and volunteers were fitted with a net of 256 electrical sensors and asked to meditate for short periods. Thinking and other mental activity are known to produce slight, but detectable, bursts of electrical activity as large groupings of neurons send messages to each other, and that's what the sensors picked up. Davidson was especially interested in measuring gamma waves, some of the highest-frequency and most important electrical brain impulses.

Both groups were asked to meditate, specifically on unconditional compassion. Buddhist teaching describes that state, which is at the heart of the Dalai Lama's teaching, as the "unrestricted readiness and availability to help living beings." The researchers chose that focus because it does not require concentrating on particular objects, memories or images, and cultivates instead a transformed state of being.

Davidson said that the results unambiguously showed that meditation activated the trained minds of the monks in significantly different ways from those of the volunteers. Most important, the electrodes picked up much greater activation of fast-moving and unusually powerful gamma waves in the monks, and found that the movement of the waves through the brain was far better organized and coordinated than in the students. The meditation novices showed only a slight increase in gamma wave activity while meditating, but some of the monks produced gamma wave activity more powerful than any previously reported in a healthy person, Davidson said.

The monks who had spent the most years meditating had the highest levels of gamma waves, he added. This "dose response" -- where higher levels of a drug or activity have greater effect than lower levels -- is what researchers look for to assess cause and effect.

In previous studies, mental activities such as focus, memory, learning and consciousness were associated with the kind of enhanced neural coordination found in the monks. The intense gamma waves found in the monks have also been associated with knitting together disparate brain circuits, and so are connected to higher mental activity and heightened awareness, as well.

Davidson's research is consistent with his earlier work that pinpointed the left prefrontal cortex as a brain region associated with happiness and positive thoughts and emotions. Using functional magnetic resonance imagining (fMRI) on the meditating monks, Davidson found that their brain activity -- as measured by the EEG -- was especially high in this area.

Davidson concludes from the research that meditation not only changes the workings of the brain in the short term, but also quite possibly produces permanent changes. That finding, he said, is based on the fact that the monks had considerably more gamma wave activity than the control group even before they started meditating. A researcher at the University of Massachusetts, Jon Kabat-Zinn, came to a similar conclusion several years ago.

Researchers at Harvard and Princeton universities are now testing some of the same monks on different aspects of their meditation practice: their ability to visualize images and control their thinking. Davidson is also planning further research.

"What we found is that the trained mind, or brain, is physically different from the untrained one," he said. In time, "we'll be able to better understand the potential importance of this kind of mental training and increase the likelihood that it will be taken seriously."

More Information

"Introduction to Modern Meditation, Part II" *Explore*, Vol. 12, No. 1, 2003 by Thomas Valone (article summary) http://www.explorepub.com/articles/summaries/12_1_valone.html

Note: For centuries, yoga practitioners have spoken about the "higher vibration levels" achievable through meditation. Science has finally caught up by proving that the highest vibration (frequency) level – gamma brain waves – increase in intensity the more one meditates. The physics of advanced bioelectromagnetics and advanced spirituality have a lot in common.   - TV

How to Get Smarter, One Breath at a Time

Lisa Takeuchi Cullen
Tuesday, Jan. 10, 2006, TIME

At 4:30, when most of Wall Street is winding down, Walter Zimmermann begins a high-stakes, high-wire act conducted live before a paying audience. About 200 institutional investors—including airlines and oil companies—shell out up to $3,000 a month to catch his daily webcast on the volatile energy markets, a performance that can move hundreds of millions of dollars. "I'm not paid to be wrong—I can tell you that," Zimmermann says. But as he clicks through dozens of screens and graphics on three computers, he's the picture of focused calm. Zimmermann, 54, watched most of his peers in energy futures burn out long ago. He attributes his brain's enduring sharpness not to an intravenous espresso drip but to 40 minutes of meditation each morning and evening. The practice, he says, helps him maintain the clarity he needs for quick, insightful analysis—even approaching happy hour. "Meditation," he says, "is my secret weapon."

Everyone around the water cooler knows that meditation reduces stress. But with the aid of advanced brainscanning technology, researchers are beginning to show that meditation directly affects the function and structure of the brain, changing it in ways that appear to increase attention span, sharpen focus and improve memory.

One recent study found evidence that the daily practice of meditation thickened the parts of the brain's cerebral cortex responsible for decision making, attention and memory. Sara Lazar, a research scientist at Massachusetts General Hospital, presented preliminary results last November that showed that the gray matter of 20 men and women who meditated for just 40 minutes a day was thicker than that of people who did not. Unlike in previous studies focusing on Buddhist monks, the subjects were Boston-area workers practicing a Western-style of meditation called mindfulness or insight meditation. "We showed for the first time that you don't have to do it all day for similar results," says Lazar. What's more, her research suggests that meditation may slow the natural thinning of that section of the cortex that occurs with age.

The forms of meditation Lazar and other scientists are studying involve focusing on an image or sound or on one's breathing. Though deceptively simple, the practice seems to exercise the parts of the brain that help us pay attention. "Attention is the key to learning, and meditation helps you voluntarily regulate it," says Richard Davidson, director of the Laboratory for Affective Neuroscience at the University of Wisconsin. Since 1992, he has collaborated with the Dalai Lama to study the brains of Tibetan monks, whom he calls "the Olympic athletes of meditation." Using caps with electrical sensors placed on the monks' heads, Davidson has picked up unusually powerful gamma waves that are better synchronized in the Tibetans than they are in novice meditators. Studies have linked this gamma-wave synchrony to increased awareness.

Many people who meditate claim the practice restores their energy, allowing them to perform better at tasks that require attention and concentration. If so, wouldn't a midday nap work just as well? No, says Bruce O'Hara, associate professor of biology at the University of Kentucky. In a study to be published this year, he had college students either meditate, sleep or watch TV. Then he tested them for what psychologists call psychomotor vigilance, asking them to hit a button when a light flashed on a screen. Those who had been taught to meditate performed 10% better—"a huge jump, statistically speaking," says O'Hara. Those who snoozed did significantly worse. "What it means," O'Hara theorizes, "is that meditation may restore synapses, much like sleep but without the initial grogginess."

Not surprisingly, given those results, a growing number of corporations—including Deutsche Bank, Google and Hughes Aircraft—offer meditation classes to their workers. Jeffrey Abramson, CEO of Tower Co., a Washington-based development firm, says 75% of his staff attend free classes in transcendental meditation. Making employees sharper is only one benefit; studies say meditation also improves productivity, in large part by preventing stress-related illness and reducing absenteeism.

Another benefit for employers: meditation seems to help regulate emotions, which in turn helps people get along. "One of the most important domains meditation acts upon is emotional intelligence—a set of skills far more consequential for life success than cognitive intelligence," says Davidson. So, for a New Year's resolution that can pay big dividends at home and at the office, try this: just breathe.

Find this article at:
http://www.time.com/time/magazine/article/0,9171,1147167,00.html

Home

Current Issue

Past Issues

Sample Articles

Article Summaries

Subscription Info

Contact Us

Calendar

Links

Sponsors

Search our articles:

Verbose report

Simple report

Search

Meditation

Introduction to modern Meditation, Part II

© Copyright 2003 by Thomas Valone, MA, PE, USA
(Explore Issue: Volume 12, Number 1)

Meditation today is proven to be physiologically transforming and recommended by doctors. To review, we touched on the practice of mantra meditation, where it is recommended to stick with one mantra you choose for at least a month or more before trying another one. We also practised a powerful breathing exercise that helps awaken brain cells through oxygen therapy. The discussion of kundalini and the chakras, vital to the advanced yogi, gave a basis for the deeper benefits that can be achieved through regular meditation. Also helpful in transforming the conscious mind is the astounding changes a person can experience through the correct practice of affirmation, implanted in the subconscious or superconscious, without any extraordinary effort. Thus, as you progress in affirmation and meditation practice, you may rightly expect some or all of the following:

- An increasing sense of peacefulness during and after meditation.
- A conscious inner experience of calmness in meditation metamophosing into increasing bliss.
- A deepening of one's understanding, and finding answers to one's questions through the calm intuitive state of inner perception.
- An increasing mental and physical efficiency in one's daily life.
- Love for meditation and the desire to hold onto the peace and joy of the meditative state in preference to attraction to anything in the world.
- An expanding consciousness of compassion with the unconditional love that one feels toward his own dearest loved ones, no matter what religion, race or nationality.
- Actual contact with God, and worshiping Him as ever-new bliss felt in meditation and in His omnipresent manifestations within and beyond all creation. -
  Yogananda (Self-Realization magazine, Spring, 1992)

You may choose to take meditation lessons locally from a yoga center or through more than one correspondence courses offering meditation instructions. Dr. Carl G. Jung, founder of analytical psychology, said that yoga and meditation promise "undreamed-of possibilities." This is also the title of a free introductory booklet available from Self-Realization Fellowship, (3880 San Rafael Ave., Los Angeles, CA 90065) describing excellent and inexpensive meditation lessons, including the Kriya and Hong Sau techniques. Meditate to improve alertness, mindfulness, general health and well-being, while enhancing one's spiritual practice, whatever that may be...or as Yogananda says, "Why not unite all your smaller lights, letting them shine

Meditate on This New Finding

— *Jeff Worley, University of Kentucky, 2007*

Bruce O'Hara, associate professor of biology, with graduate students Prashant Kaul and Ling Liu, found that to enhance mental acuity meditation is more effective than a power nap.

Anybody who practices the ancient art of meditation will tell you it helps them feel more relaxed and attentive. But does it also enhance performance?

Bruce O'Hara, an associate professor of biology at the University of Kentucky, and graduate student Prashant Kaul wanted to find out, so they devised a study to see how meditation might affect the ability to do a boring task during the mid-afternoon, a time when attention often flags. O'Hara and Kaul used a "psychomotor vigilance task," which has long been used to quantify the effects of sleepiness on mental acuity. The test involves staring at a computer screen and pressing a button as soon as a lighted image pops up.

Typically, people take 200 to 300 milliseconds to respond, but sleep-deprived people take much longer, and sometimes miss the stimulus altogether. Ten UK students were tested before and after 40 minutes of either sleep, meditation, reading, or light conversation, with all subjects trying all conditions.

The results surprised O'Hara. "We found that meditation was the only intervention that immediately led to superior performance, even though none of the volunteers were experienced at meditation. Every single student who meditated showed improvement," says O'Hara. But, he admits, "Why it improves performance, we don't know."

But what about the heralded power nap? Didn't it fare at least as well as meditation?

"No, everybody got worse with a nap," says O'Hara, "because we had the volunteers start the test immediately after they woke up. A 40-minute nap does tend to improve performance, but only after an hour or so to recover from grogginess."

http://www.research.uky.edu/odyssey/winter07/meditation.html

Long-Term Meditators Self-Induce High-Amplitude Gamma Synchrony During Mental Practice

NEUROSCIENCE

PNAS | November 16, 2004 | vol. 101 | no. 46 | 16369-16373

Antoine Lutz *, , Lawrence L. Greischar *, Nancy B. Rawlings *, Matthieu Ricard and Richard J. Davidson *,

*W. M. Keck Laboratory for Functional Brain Imaging and Behavior, Waisman Center, and Laboratory for Affective Neuroscience, Department of Psychology, University of Wisconsin, 1500 Highland Avenue, Madison, WI 53705; and Shechen Monastery, P.O. Box 136, Kathmandu, Nepal

Communicated by Burton H. Singer, Princeton University, Princeton, NJ, October 6, 2004 (received for review August 26, 2004)

Published online before print November 8, 2004, 10.1073/pnas.0407401101
OPEN ACCESS ARTICLE

http://www.pnas.org/cgi/content/full/101/46/16369?maxtoshow=&HIT
S=10&hits=10&RESULTFORMAT=&fulltext=10.1073%2Fpnas.0407
401101+&searchid=1124835633286_9722&stored_search=&FIRSTIN
DEX=0&journalcode=pnas

Abstract

Practitioners understand "meditation," or mental training, to be a process of familiarization with one's own mental life leading to long-lasting changes in cognition and emotion. Little is known about this process and its impact on the brain. Here we find that long-term Buddhist practitioners self-induce sustained electroencephalographic high-amplitude gamma-band oscillations and phase-synchrony during meditation. These electroencephalogram patterns differ from those of controls, in particular over lateral frontoparietal electrodes. In addition, the ratio of gamma-band activity (25-42 Hz) to slow oscillatory activity (4-13 Hz) is initially higher in the resting baseline before meditation for the practitioners than the controls over medial frontoparietal electrodes. This difference increases sharply during meditation over most of the scalp electrodes and remains higher than the initial baseline in the postmeditation baseline. These data suggest that mental training involves temporal integrative mechanisms and may induce short-term and long-term neural changes.

electroencephalogram synchrony | gamma activity | meditation

Little is known about the process of meditation and its impact on the brain (1, 2). Previous studies show the general role of neural synchrony, in particular in the gamma-band frequencies (25-70Hz), in mental processes such as attention, working-memory, learning, or conscious perception (3-7). Such synchronizations of oscillatory neural discharges are thought to play a crucial role in the constitution of transient networks that integrate distributed neural processes into highly ordered cognitive and affective functions (8, 9) and could induce synaptic changes (10, 11). Neural synchrony thus appears as a promising mechanism for the study of brain processes underlining mental training.

Methods

The subjects were eight long-term Buddhist practitioners (mean age, 49 ± 15 years) and 10 healthy student volunteers (mean age, 21 ± 1.5 years). Buddhist practitioners underwent mental training in the same Tibetan Nyingmapa and Kagyupa traditions for 10,000 to 50,000 h over time periods ranging from 15 to 40 years. The length of their training was estimated based on their daily practice and the time they spent in meditative retreats. Eight hours of sitting meditation was counted per day of retreat. Control subjects had no previous meditative experience but had declared an interest in meditation. Controls underwent meditative training for 1 week before the collection of the data.

We first collected an initial electroencephalogram (EEG) baseline consisting of four 60-s blocks of ongoing activity with a balanced random ordering of eyes open or closed for each block. Then, subjects generated three meditative states, only one of which will be described in this report. During each meditative session, a 30-s block of resting activity and a 60-s block of meditation were collected four times sequentially. The subjects were verbally instructed to begin the meditation and meditated at least 20 s before the start of the meditation block. We focus here on the last objectless meditative practice during which both the controls and Buddhist practitioners generated a state of "unconditional loving-kindness and compassion."

Meditative Instruction. The state of unconditional loving-kindness and compassion is described as an "unrestricted readiness and availability to help living beings." This practice does not require concentration on particular objects, memories, or images, although in other meditations that are also part of their long-term training, practitioners focus on particular persons or groups of beings. Because "benevolence and compassion pervades the mind as a way of being," this state is called "pure compassion" or "nonreferential compassion" (dmigs med snying rje in Tibetan). A week before the collection of the data, meditative instructions were given to the control subjects, who were asked to practice daily for 1 h. The quality of their training was verbally assessed before EEG collection. During the training session, the control subjects were asked to think of someone they care about, such as their parents or beloved, and to let their mind be invaded by a feeling of love or compassion (by imagining a sad situation and wishing freedom from suffering and well being for those involved) toward these persons. After some training, the subjects were asked to generate such feeling toward all sentient beings without thinking specifically about anyone in particular. During the EEG data collection period, both controls and long-term practitioners tried to generate this nonreferential state of loving-kindness and compassion. During the neutral states, all of the subjects were asked to be in a nonmeditative, relaxed state.

EEG Recordings and Protocol. EEG data were recorded at standard extended 10/20 positions with a 128-channel Geodesic Sensor Net (Electrical Geodesics, Eugene, OR), sampled at 500 Hz, and referenced to the vertex (Cz) with analog band-pass filtering between 0.1 and 200 Hz. EEG signals showing eye movements or muscular artifacts were manually excluded from the study. A digital notch filter was applied to the data at 60 Hz to remove any artifacts caused by alternating current line noise.

Bad channels were replaced by using spherical spline interpolation (12). Two-second epochs without artifact were extracted after the digital rereferencing to the average reference.

Spectral Analysis. For each electrode and for each 2-s epoch, the power spectral distribution was computed by using Welch's method (13), which averages power values across sliding and overlapping 512-ms time windows. To compute the relative gamma activity, the power spectral distribution was computed on the z-transformed EEG by using the mean and SD of the signal in each 2-s window. This distribution was averaged through all electrodes, and the ratio between gamma and slow rhythms was computed. Intraindividual analyses were run on this measure and a group analysis was run on the average ratio across 2-s windows. The group analysis of the topography was performed by averaging the power spectral distribution for each electrode in each block and then computing the ratio of gamma to slow rhythms before averaging across blocks.

Despite careful visual examination, the electroencephalographic spectral analysis was hampered by the possible contamination of brain signals by muscle activity. Here we assume that the spectral emission between 80 and 120 Hz provided an adequate measure of the muscle activity (14, 15). The muscle EEG signature is characterized by a broad-band spectrum profile (8-150 Hz) peaking at 70-80 Hz (16). Thus, the variation through time of the average spectral power in the 80-120 Hz frequency band provided a way to quantify the variations of the muscle contribution to the EEG gamma activity through time. To estimate the gamma activity, adjusted for the very high frequencies, we performed a covariance analysis for each region of interest (ROI) for each subject. The dependent variable was the average gamma activity (25-42 Hz) in each ROI. The continuous predictor was the electromyogram activity (80-120 Hz power). The categorical predictors were the blocks (initial baseline with eyes open and neutral blocks from 2 to 4) and the mental states (ongoing neutral versus meditation).

For the group analysis, separate repeated ANOVAs were then performed on the relative gamma and adjusted gamma variation between states, with the blocks as the within factor and the group (practitioners versus controls) as the categorical predictor. For the intrasubject analysis, we compared separately the relative gamma and the raw gamma activity averaged within the ROIs in the initial baseline state versus the meditative state.

Phase-Synchrony Detection. Electrodes of interest were referenced to a local average potential defined as the average potential of its six surrounding neighbors. This referencing montage restricted the electrical measurement to local sources only and prevented spurious long-range synchrony from being detected if the muscle activity over one electrode propagated to another distant electrode. The methods used to measure long-range synchronization are described in detail in Supporting Methods, which is published as supporting information on the PNAS web site. In summary, for each epoch and electrode, the instantaneous phase of the signal was extracted at each frequency band between 25 and 42 Hz in 2-Hz steps by using a convolution with Morlet wavelets. The stability through time of their phase difference was quantified in comparison with white-noise signals as independent surrogates. A measure of synchronous activity was defined as the number of electrode pairs among the 294 studied combinations that had higher synchrony density on average across frequencies than would be expected to occur between independent signals. The electrode pairs were taken between the ROIs when we measured the scalp distribution of gamma activity (see Fig. 3a). A repeated-measures ANOVA was performed on the average size of the synchrony pattern across all frequency bands and epochs in each block with the original resting state and the meditative state as the within factors and the group (practitioners versus controls) as the between-groups factor.

Fig. 3. Absolute gamma power and long-distance synchrony during mental training. (a) Scalp distribution of gamma activity during meditation. The color scale indicates the percentage of subjects in each group that had an increase of gamma activity during the mental training. (Left) Controls. (Right) Practitioners. An increase was defined as a change in average gamma activity of >1 SD during the meditative state compared with the neutral state. Black circles indicate the electrodes of interest for the group analysis. (b) Adjusted gamma variation between neutral and meditative states over electrodes F3-8, Fc3-6, T7-8, Tp7-10, and P7-10 for controls and long-time practitioners [$F(1, 16) = 4.6$, $P < 0.05$; ANOVA]. (c) Interaction between the group and state variables for the number of electrode pairs between ROIs that exhibited synchrony higher than noise surrogates [$F(1, 16) = 6.5$, $P < 0.05$; ANOVA]. The blue line represents the controls; the red line represents the practitioners. (d) Correlation between the length of the long-term practitioners' meditation training and the ratio of relative gamma activity averaged across electrodes in

73

the initial baseline (P < 0.02). Dotted lines represent 95% confidence intervals.

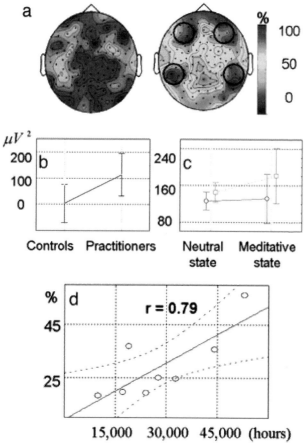

Results

We first computed the power spectrum density over each electrode in the EEG signals visually free from artifacts. This procedure was adapted to detect change in local synchronization (6, 9). Local synchronization occurs when neurons recorded by a single electrode transiently oscillate at the same frequency with a common phase: Their local electric field adds up to produce a burst of oscillatory power in the signal reaching the electrode. Thus, the power spectral density provides an estimation of the average of these peaks of energy in a time window. During meditation, we found high-amplitude gamma oscillations in the EEGs of long-time practitioners (subjects S1-S8) that were not present in the initial baseline. Fig. 1a provides a representative example of the raw EEG signal (25-42 Hz) for subject S4. An essential aspect of these gamma oscillations is that their amplitude monotonically increased over the time of the practice (Fig. 1b).

Fig. 1. High-amplitude gamma activity during mental training. (a) Raw electroencephalographic signals. At t = 45 s, practitioner S4 started generating a state of nonreferential compassion, block 1. (b)

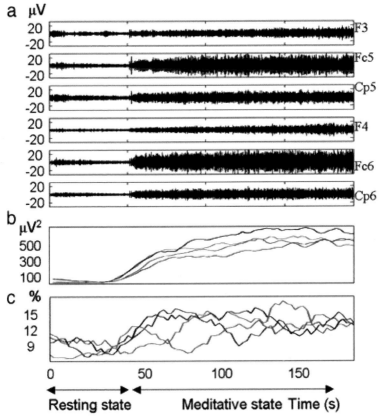

Time course of gamma activity power over the electrodes displayed in a during four blocks computed in a 20-s sliding window every 2 s and then averaged over electrodes. (c) Time course of subjects' cross-hemisphere synchrony between 25 and 42 Hz. The density of long-distance synchrony above a surrogate threshold was calculated in a 20-s sliding window every 2 s for each cross-hemisphere electrode pair and was then averaged across electrode pairs (see Methods). Colors denote different trial blocks: blue, block 1; red, block 2; green, block 3; black, block 4.

Relative Gamma Power. We characterized these changes in gamma oscillations in relation to the slow rhythms (4-13 Hz) that are thought to play a complementary function to fast rhythms (3). Fig. 2a shows the intraindividual analysis of this ratio averaged through all electrodes. This ratio, which was averaged across all electrodes, presented an increase compared with the initial baseline, which was greater than twice the baseline SD for two controls and all of the practitioners. The ratio of gamma-band activity (25-42 Hz) compared to slow rhythms was initially higher in the baseline before meditation for the practitioners compared with the controls ($t = 4.0$, $df = 16$, $P < 0.001$; t test) (Fig. 2b). This effect remained when we compared the three youngest practitioners with the controls (25, 34, and 36 years old, respectively) ($t = 2.2$, $df = 11$, $P < 0.05$; t test). This result suggests that the mean age difference between groups does not fully account for this baseline difference (17).

Fig. 2. Relative gamma power during mental training. (a and b) Intraindividual analysis on the ratio of gamma (25-42 Hz) to slow (4-13 Hz) oscillations averaged through all electrodes. (a) The abscissa represents the subject numbers, the ordinate represents the difference in the mean ratio between the initial state and meditative state, and the black and red stars indicate that this increase is >2- and 3-fold, respectively, the baseline SD. (b) Interaction between the subject and the state factors for this ratio [$F(2, 48) = 3.5$, $P < 0.05$; ANOVA]. IB, initial baseline; OB, ongoing baseline; MS, meditative state. (c-e)

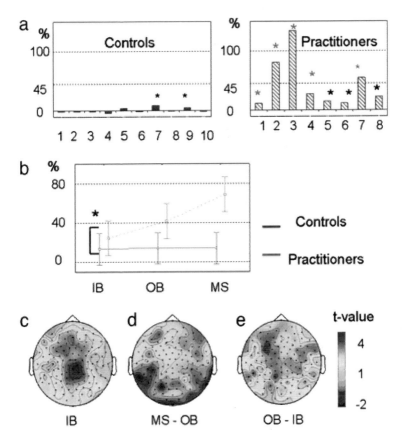

Comparisons of this ratio between controls and practitioners over each electrode [t > 2.6, P < 0.01, scaling (-2.5, 4); t test] during the premeditative initial baseline (c), between the ongoing baseline and the meditative state (d), and between the ongoing baseline and the initial baseline (e).

This baseline difference increased sharply during meditation, as revealed by an interaction between the state and group factors [$F(2, 48)$ = 3.7, P < 0.05; ANOVA] (Fig. 2b). This difference was still found in comparisons between gamma activity and both theta (4-8 Hz) and alpha activity. To localize these differences on the scalp, similar analyses were performed on each individual electrode. Fig. 2c shows a higher ratio of fast versus slow oscillations for the long-term practitioners versus the controls in the initial baseline over medial frontoparietal electrodes (t > 2.59, P = 0.01; t test). Similarly, Fig. 2d shows a group difference between the ongoing baseline states and the meditative state, in particular over the frontolateral and posterior electrodes. Interestingly, the postmeditative baseline (neutral states in blocks 2, 3, and 4) also revealed a significant increase in this ratio compared with the premeditation baseline over mainly anterior electrodes (Fig. 2e).

These data suggest that the two groups had different electrophysiological spectral profiles in the baseline, which are characterized by a higher ratio of gamma-band oscillatory rhythm to slow oscillatory rhythms for the long-term practitioners than for the controls. This group difference is enhanced during the meditative practice and continues into the postmeditative resting blocks.

Absolute Gamma Power. We then studied the variation through time of the ongoing gamma-band activity itself. The gamma-band activity (25-42 Hz) was first z-transformed in each block and compared over each electrode with the mean and SD of their respective neutral block (ongoing baseline). The normalized gamma activity was then averaged across the blocks. Fig. 3a shows the percentage of subjects presenting an increase of at least 1 SD during meditation compared with neutral state. A common topographical pattern of gamma activity emerged across the long-term practitioners but not across the control subjects. This pattern was located bilaterally over the parieto-temporal and midfrontal electrodes. Fig. 3a shows four ROIs containing seven electrodes each and located around F3-8, Fc3-6, T7-8, Tp7-10, and P7-10. Hereafter, we focus on the electrodes activated in these ROIs.

Intraindividual analyses similar to those for relative gamma activity were run on the average gamma power across these ROIs and exhibited the same pattern as that found for relative gamma. It is possible that these high-amplitude oscillations are partially contaminated by muscle activity (18). Because we found increases in gamma activity during the postmeditative resting baseline compared with the initial resting baseline, it is unlikely that the changes we reported could be solely caused by muscle activity, because there was little evidence of any muscle activity during these baseline periods. (Fig. 2e). Secondly, we showed that the meditative state and nonmeditative state that mimicked and exaggerated the possible muscle activity during meditation exhibit significantly different spectral profiles (Fig. 4, which is published as supporting information on the PNAS web site). Furthermore, for the two subjects showing the highest gamma activity, we showed that amplitude of the gamma-band activity before external stimulation predicts the amplitude of high fast-frequency oscillations (20-45 Hz) evoked by auditory stimuli (Fig. 5, which is published as supporting information on the PNAS web site). Because the evoked activity is relatively independent of muscle activity, the relationship between the pre-stimulation fast-frequency oscillation and the evoked activity suggests that these high-amplitude gamma rhythms are not muscle artifacts (Fig. 5 and Fig. 6, which is published as supporting information on the PNAS web site). This claim is further supported by the localization within the brain of the dipole sources of these fast-frequency-evoked oscillations (Figs. 7-9, which are published as supporting information on the PNAS web site).

Yet we still chose to cautiously interpret the raw values of these gamma oscillations because of the concomitant increase of spectral power >80 Hz during meditation. This increase could also reflect a change in muscle activity rather than high-frequency, gamma-band oscillations [70-105 Hz (19)], which are mostly low-pass filtered by the skull at >80 Hz. Thus, we chose to conservatively interpret the activity at >80 Hz as indicating muscle activity.

To remove the contribution of putative muscle activity, we quantified the increase in the average amplitude of gamma oscillation (25-42 Hz) adjusted for the effect of the very high-frequency variation (80-120 Hz) (see Methods and ref. 20). The adjusted average variation in gamma activity was >30-fold greater among practitioners compared with controls (Fig. 3b). Group analysis was run on the average adjusted gamma activity over these ROIs. Gamma activity increased for both the long-term practitioners and controls from neutral to meditation states $[F(1, 16) = 5.2, P < 0.05;$ ANOVA], yet this increase was higher for the long-time practitioners than for the controls $[F(1, 16) = 4.6, P < 0.05;$ interaction between the state and group factors ANOVA] (Fig. 3b). In summary, the generation of this meditative state was associated with gamma oscillations that were significantly higher in amplitude for the group of practitioners than for the group of control subjects.

Long-Distance Gamma Synchrony. Finally, a long-distance synchrony analysis was conducted between electrodes from the ROIs found in Fig. 3a. Long-distance synchrony is thought to reflect large-scale neural coordination (9) and can occur when two neural populations recorded by two distant electrodes oscillate with a precise phase relationship that remains constant during a certain number of oscillation cycles. This approach is illustrated in Fig. 1c for selected electrodes (F3/4, Fc5/6, and Cp5/6). For subject S4, the density of cross-hemisphere, long-distance synchrony increases by 30% on average during meditation and follows a pattern similar to the oscillatory gamma activity.

For all subjects, locally referenced, long-distance synchronies were computed for each 2-s epoch during the neutral and meditative states between all electrode pairs and across eight frequencies ranging from 25 to 42 Hz. In each meditative or neutral block, we counted the number of electrode pairs (294 electrode pairs maximum) that had an average density of synchrony higher than those derived from noise surrogates (see Methods). We ran a group analysis on the size of the synchronous pattern and found that its size was greater for long-time practitioners than for controls [$F(1, 16) = 10.3$, $P < 0.01$; ANOVA] and increased from neutral to meditation states [$F(1, 16) = 8.2$, $P < 0.02$; ANOVA]. Fig. 3c shows that the group and state factors interacted on long-distance synchrony [$F(1, 16) = 6.5$, $P < 0.05$; ANOVA]: The size of synchrony patterns increased more for the long-time practitioners than for the controls from neutral to meditation states. These data suggest that large-scale brain coordination increases during mental practice.

Finally, we investigated whether there was a correlation between the hours of formal sitting meditation (for subjects S1-S8, 9,855-52,925 h) and these electrophysiological measures for the long-term practitioners, in either the initial or meditative states (same values as in Figs. 2 and 3). The correlation coefficients for the relative, absolute, and phase-synchrony gamma measures were positive: $r = 0.79$, 0.63, and 0.64, respectively, in the initial state, and $r = 0.66$, 0.62, and 0.43, respectively, in the meditative state. A significant positive correlation was found only in the initial baseline for the relative gamma ($r = 0.79$, $P < 0.02$) (Fig. 3d). These data suggest that the degree of training can influence the spectral distribution of the ongoing baseline EEG. The age of the subject was not a confounding factor in this effect as suggested by the low correlation between the practitioner age and the relative gamma ($r = 0.23$).

Discussion

We found robust gamma-band oscillation and long-distance phase-synchrony during the generation of the nonreferential compassion meditative state. It is likely based on descriptions of various meditation practices and mental strategies that are reported by practitioners that there will be differences in brain function associated with different types of meditation. In light of our initial observations concerning robust gamma oscillations during this compassion meditation state, we focused our initial attention on this state. Future research is required to characterize the nature of the differences among types of meditation. Our resulting data differ from several studies that found an increase in slow alpha or theta rhythms during meditation (21). The comparison is limited by the fact that these studies typically did not analyze fast rhythms. More importantly, these studies mainly investigated different forms of voluntary concentrative meditation on an object (such as a meditation on a mantra or the breath). These concentration techniques can be seen as a particular form of top-down control that may exhibit an important slow oscillatory component (22). First-person descriptions of objectless meditations, however, differ radically from those of concentration meditation. Objectless meditation does not directly attend to a specific object but rather cultivates a state of being. Objectless meditation does so in such a way that, according to reports given after meditation, the intentional or object-oriented aspect of experience appears to dissipate in meditation. This dissipation of focus on a particular object is achieved by letting the very essence of the meditation that is practiced (on compassion in this case) become the sole content of the experience, without focusing on particular objects. By using similar techniques during the practice, the practitioner lets his feeling of loving-kindness and compassion permeate his mind without directing his attention toward a particular object. These phenomenological differences suggest that these various meditative states (those that involve focus on an object and those that are objectless) may be associated with different EEG oscillatory signatures.

The high-amplitude gamma activity found in some of these practitioners are, to our knowledge, the highest reported in the literature in a nonpathological context (23). Assuming that the amplitude of the gamma oscillation is related to the size of the oscillating neural population and the degree of precision with which cells oscillate, these data suggest that massive distributed neural assemblies are synchronized with a high temporal precision in the fast frequencies during this state. The gradual increase of gamma activity during meditation is in agreement with the view that neural synchronization, as a network phenomenon, requires time to develop (24), proportional to the size of the synchronized neural assembly (25). But this increase could also reflect an increase in the temporal precision of the thalamo-cortical and corticocortical interactions rather than a change in the size of the assemblies (8). This gradual increase also corroborates the Buddhist subjects' verbal report of the chronometry of their practice. Typically, the transition from the neutral state to this meditative state is not immediate and requires 5-15 s, depending on the subject. The endogenous gamma-band synchrony found here could reflect a change in the quality of moment-to-moment awareness, as claimed by the Buddhist practitioners and as postulated by many models of consciousness (26, 27).

In addition to the meditation-induced effects, we found a difference in the normative EEG spectral profile between the two populations during the resting state before meditation. It is not unexpected that such differences would be detected during a resting baseline, because the goal of meditation practice is to transform the baseline state and to diminish the distinction between formal meditation practice and everyday life. Moreover, Gusnard and Raichle (28) have highlighted the importance of characteristic patterns of brain activity during the resting state and argue that such patterns affect the nature of task-induced changes. The differences in baseline activity reported here suggest that the resting state of the brain may be altered by long-term meditative practice and imply that such alterations may affect task-related changes. Our practitioners and control subjects differed in many respects, including age, culture of origin, and first language, and they likely differed in many more respects, including diet and sleep. We examined whether age was an important factor in producing the baseline differences we observed by comparing the three youngest practitioners with the controls and found that the mean age difference between groups is unlikely the sole factor responsible for this baseline difference. Moreover, hours of practice but not age significantly predicted relative gamma activity during the initial baseline period. Whether other demographic factors are important in producing these effects will necessarily require further research, particularly longitudinal research that follows individuals over time in response to mental training.

Our study is consistent with the idea that attention and affective processes, which gamma-band EEG synchronization may reflect, are flexible skills that can be trained (29). It remains for future studies to show that these EEG signatures are caused by long-term training itself and not by individual differences before the training, although the positive correlation that we found with hours of training and other randomized controlled trials suggest that these are training-related effects (2). The functional consequences of sustained gamma-activity during mental practice are not currently known but need to be studied in the future. The study of experts in mental training may offer a promising research strategy to investigate high-order cognitive and affective processes (30).

Acknowledgements

We thank J. Dunne for Tibetan translation; A. Shah, A. Francis, and J. Hanson for assistance in data collection and preanalysis; the long-time Buddhist practitioners who participated in the study; J.-Ph. Lachaux, J. Martinerie, W. Singer, and G. Tononi and his team for suggestions on the manuscript; F. Varela for early inspirations; and His Holiness the Dalai Lama for his encouragement and advice in the conducting of this research. We also thank the Mind and Life Institute for providing the initial contacts and support to make this research possible. This research was supported by National Institute of Mental Health Mind-Body Center Grant P50-MH61083, the Fyssen Foundation, and a gift from Edwin Cook and Adrianne Ryder-Cook.

Footnotes

Author contributions: A.L., M.R., and R.J.D. designed research; A.L. and N.B.R. performed research; A.L. and L.L.G. analyzed data; and A.L. and R.J.D. wrote the paper.

Freely available online through the PNAS open access option.

Abbreviations: ROI, region of interest; EEG, electroencephalogram.

To whom correspondence may be addressed. E-mail: alutz@wisc.edu or rjdavids@wisc.edu.

References

Austin, J. H. (1998) Zen and the Brain: Toward an Understanding of Meditation and Consciousness (MIT Press, Cambridge, MA).

Davidson, R. J., Kabat-Zinn, J., Schumacher, J., Rosenkranz, M., Muller, D., Santorelli, S. F., Urbanowski, F., Harrington, A., Bonus, K. & Sheridan, J. F. (2003) Psychosom. Med. 65, 564-570.[Abstract/Free Full Text]

Fries, P., Reynolds, J. H., Rorie, A. E. & Desimone, R. (2001) Science 291, 1560-1563.[Abstract/Free Full Text]

Miltner, W. H., Braun, C., Arnold, M., Witte, H. & Taub, E. (1999) Nature 397, 434-436.[CrossRef][ISI][Medline]

Srinivasan, R., Russell, D. P., Edelman, G. M. & Tononi, G. (1999) J. Neurosci. 19, 5435-5448.[Abstract/Free Full Text]

Tallon-Baudry, C., Bertrand, O., Peronnet, F. & Pernier, J. (1998) J. Neurosci. 18, 4244-4254.[Abstract/Free Full Text]

Rodriguez, E., George, N., Lachaux, J. P., Martinerie, J., Renault, B. & Varela, F. J. (1999) Nature 397, 430-433.[CrossRef][ISI][Medline]

Singer, W. (1999) Neuron 24, 49-65.[ISI][Medline]

Varela, F., Lachaux, J. P., Rodriguez, E. & Martinerie, J. (2001) Nat. Rev. Neurosci. 2, 229-239.[CrossRef][ISI][Medline]

Hebb, D. O. (1949) The Organization of Behavior: A Neuropsychological Theory (Wiley, New York).

Paulsen, O., Sejnowski, T. J. (2000) Curr. Opin. Neurobiol. 10, 172-179.[CrossRef][ISI][Medline]

Perrin, F., Pernier, J., Bertrand, O. & Echallier, J. F. (1989) Electroencephalogr. Clin. Neurophysiol. 72, 184-187.[CrossRef][ISI][Medline]

Welch, P. D. (1967) IEEE Trans. Audio Electroacoust. 15, 70-73.

Davidson, R. J., Marshall, J. R., Tomarken, A. J. & Henriques, J. B. (2000) Biol. Psychiatry 47, 85-95.[CrossRef][ISI][Medline]

Pivik, R. T., Broughton, R. J., Coppola, R., Davidson, R. J., Fox, N. & Nuwer, M. R. (1993) Psychophysiology 30, 547-558.[ISI][Medline]

Cacioppo, J. T., Tassinary, L. G. & Fridlund, A. J. (1990) in Principles of Psychophysiology, ed. Tassinary, L. G. (Cambridge Univ. Press, New York), pp. 325-384.

Duffy, F. H., Albert, M. S., McAnulty, G. & Garvey, A. J. (1984) Ann. Neurol. 16, 430-438.[ISI][Medline]

Goncharova, I. I., McFarland, D. J., Vaughan, T. M. & Wolpaw, J. R. (2003) Clin. Neurophysiol. 114, 1580-1593.[CrossRef][ISI][Medline]

Herculano-Houzel, S., Munk, M. H., Neuenschwander, S. & Singer, W. (1999) J. Neurosci. 19, 3992-4010.[Abstract/Free Full Text]

Davidson, R. J., Jackson, D. C. & Larson, L. C. (2000) in Handbook of Psychophysiology (Cambridge Univ. Press, New York), pp. 27-52.

Shapiro, D. H. (1980) Meditation: Self-Regulation Strategy and Altered State of Consciousness (Aldine, New York).

von Stein, A., Chiang, C. & Konig, P. (2000) Proc. Natl. Acad. Sci. USA 97, 14748-14753.[Abstract/Free Full Text]

Baldeweg, T., Spence, S., Hirsch, S. R. & Gruzelier, J. (1998) Lancet 352, 620-621.[ISI][Medline]

Kuramato, Y. (1975) in International Symposium on Mathematical Problems in Theoretical Physics, ed. Araki, H. (Springer, New York), Vol. 39, pp. 420.

Campbell, S. R., Wang, D. L. & Jayaprakash, C. (1999) Neural Comput. 11, 1595-1619.[Abstract/Free Full Text]

Tononi, G. & Edelman, G. M. (1998) Science 282, 1846-1851.[Abstract/Free Full Text]

Engel, A. K., Fries, P., Konig, P., Brecht, M. & Singer, W. (1999) Conscious. Cognit. 8, 128-151.[CrossRef][ISI][Medline]

Gusnard, D. A. & Raichle, M. E. (2001) Nat. Rev. Neurosci. 2, 685-694.[CrossRef][ISI][Medline]

Posner, M. I., DiGirolamo, G. J. & Fernandez-Duque, D. (1997) Conscious. Cognit. 6, 267-290.[CrossRef][ISI]

Lutz, A. & Thompson, E. (2003) J. Conscious. Stud. 10, 31-52.

This article has been cited by other articles in HighWire Press-hosted journals:

"Practice Makes Perfect?"
Journal Watch Psychiatry, December 8, 2004; 2004(1208): 6 - 6.
[Full Text]

What Are the Benefits of Meditation?
Lorin Roche
http://www.lorinroche.com/page4/page4.html

Meditation is supposed to be good for you. Is this true?

Let's look at some research. Over the past 40 years, dozens of universities in the United States, Europe and India have conducted hundreds of studies on the effects of meditation on human physiology and behavior. The research (link to Institute for Noetic Sciences, www.noetic.org) results point to meditation as producing benefits on many levels of life simultaneously – body, emotions, mental functioning, and relationships.

· Greater Orderliness of Brain Functioning
· Improved Ability to Focus
· Increased Creativity
· Deeper Level of Relaxation
· Improved Perception and Memory
· Development of Intelligence
· Natural Change in Breathing
· Decrease in Stress Hormone
· Lower Blood Pressure
· Reversal of Aging Process
· Reduced Need for Medical Care
· Reduction in Cholesterol
· Increased Self-Actualization
· Increased Strength of Self-Concept
· Decreased Cigarette, Alcohol, and Drug Abuse
· Increased Productivity
· Improved Relations at Work
· Increased Relaxation and Decreased Stress
· Improved Health and More Positive Health Habits

(*The above list is culled from the advertising-promotion section over at tm.org, an official website of the Transcendental Meditation organization. It is a summary of research conducted at many universities from 1970 to the present).

What's the catch? The catch is, you have to spend time in meditation everyday to get these benefits. And usually, in order for that to happen, you have to want to meditate, and that means the approach you choose has to suit your individual nature so well that you love meditating.

Over the years, when interviewing people who quit meditating, it appears that they quit because they were doing the wrong technique, not because they were undisciplined.

There are thousands of different ways and styles of meditating. This is because people are really, really different from each other. Unfortunately, this means that if you just randomly try this and that meditation you may not find an approach that works for you. The success ratio is so low that no one seems to even be studying it – but it may be as low as 5% or even 3% of people who start. Instinctive Meditation was created in part out of the study of how and why people fail at meditation. We interviewed hundreds of meditators of all kinds in the 1970's to find out what went wrong, and developed a system of instruction that lets people have a good chance of getting it right the first time.

How Can Meditation Be This Beneficial?

It is interesting to wonder, how could something as simple as meditation be so beneficial? The answer is in the physiology. Meditation is something the body knows how to do, and does willingly if you set up the conditions and allow it. The body knows how to enter a profound healing state. All you have to do is pay attention in certain ways, and tolerate the intensity of what you feel as you let go of stress.

So one answer is that meditation is a built-in ability of the human body. The word meditation is just a name we give to the situation where we give the nervous system, the brain and senses a chance to tune themselves up. More than a chance – meditation is giving total permission for the nervous system to do its healing thing. And since this is an innate thing, the body and brain are very good at it. People are naturally good at meditation, like cats are naturally good at hunting mice.

And when we don't meditate, it is as if we are "meditation-deprived." In other words, we are not adding something weird to our life – we are just giving ourselves something we need. What is weird is to NOT meditate. In other words, it is unnatural to go through life deprived of a time each day to rest more deeply than sleep, and let go of all the stresses that keep you wound so tight.

If this is true, then this is part of why meditation has such powerful effects – because it is a way of giving into the powerful mind/body healing dynamics that we already have within us, as part of our genetic heritage. Or, you could say, God put it there.

Meditation is one of the few things in the self-help arena you can do that produces measurable changes. In other words, you can take a few hours of meditation training, and then go into a medical lab and meditate, and they can meaure the changes in your breathing, your blood chemistry, your brain waves, and your response to stress. And if you were sitting in a medical lab, all wired up, and they saw you enter a state of rest deeper than sleep in 5 minutes, a knowledgable researcher would look at the instruments and say, "Oh, you just started meditating. I can see it on the meters."

One of the main reasons meditation is so beneficial is that it is instinctive and natural. When you meditate, you are accessing your body's own built-in ability to heal itself and tune itself for action.

Here is a summary of research findings cited at the Mind Body Medical Institute at Harvard Medical School (They recently changed the name to **Benson-Henry Institute for Mind-Body Medicine**. *BHIMBM*

Mind/Body Medical Institute clinical findings include:

Chronic pain patients reduce their physician visits by 36%.
The Clinical Journal of Pain, Volume 2, pages 305-310, 1991

There is approximately a 50% reduction in visits to a HMO after a relaxation-response based intervention which resulted in estimated significant cost savings.
Behavioral Medicine, Volume 16, pages 165-173, 1990

Eighty percent of hypertensive patients have lowered blood pressure and decreased medications - 16% are able to discontinue all of their medications. These results lasted at least three years.
Journal of Cardiopulmonary Rehabilitation, Volume 9, pages 316-324, 1989

Open heart surgery patients have fewer post-operative complications.
Behavioral Medicine, Volume 5, pages 111-117, 1989

One-hundred percent of insomnia patients reported improved sleep and 91% either eliminated or reduced sleeping medication use.
The American Journal of Medicine, Volume 100, pages 212-216, 1996

Infertile women have a 42% conception rate, a 38% take-home baby rate, and decreased levels of depression, anxiety, and anger.
Journal of American Medical Women's Association. Volume 54, pages 196-8, 1999

Women with severe PMS have a 57% reduction in physical and psychological symptoms.
Obstetrics and Gynecology, Volume 75, pages 649-655, April, 1990

High school students exposed to a relaxation response-based curriculum had significantly increased their self-esteem.
The Journal of Research and Development in Education, Volume 27, pages 226-231, 1994

Inner city middle school students improved grade score, work habits and cooperation and decreased absences.
Journal of Research and Development in Education, Volume 33, pages 156-165, Spring 2000

You can read more about MBMI's approach to research here.

The following list of research is interesting, and most of the results will probably be proven to some extent in the future, but right now this is a mixure of preliminary results and solid data.

Greater Orderliness of Brain Functioning

EEG coherence increases between and within the cerebral hemispheres during meditation. EEG coherence is quantitative index of the degree of long-range spatial ordering of the brain waves. In a new meditator, the EEG coherence increased during the period of meditation. In a person who had been meditating for 2 years, spreading of coherence occurred even before meditation began, spreading of coherence to high and lower frequencies about half way through the meditation period, and continuing high coherence even into the eyes-opened period after meditation. Psychosomatic Medicine 46: 267-276, 1984.

Broader Comprehension and Improved Ability to Focus

Field independence has been associated with a greater ability to assimilate and structure experience, greater organization of mind and cognitive clarity, improved memory, greater creative expression, and a stable internal frame of reference. The results show that practice of meditation techniques develop greater field independence. This improvement in meditators is remarkable because it was previously thought that these basic perceptual abilities do not improve beyond early adulthood. Perceptual Motor Skills 39: 1031-1034, 1974, and 62: 731-738, 1986.

Increased Creativity

This study used the Torrance Test of Creative Thinking to measure figural and verbal creativity in a control group and in a group that subsequently learned meditation. On the post test five months later, the meditation group scored significantly higher on figural originality and flexibility and on verbal fluency. Journal of Creative Behavior, 13: 169-190, 1979, and Dissertations Abstracts International, 38: 3372-3373, 1978.

Deeper Level of Relaxation

A comprehensive statistical "meta-analysis" was conducted that compared the findings of 31 physiological studies on meditation and on resting with eyes closed. (A meta-analysis is the preferred scientific procedure for drawing definitive conclusions from large bodies of research). The study evaluated three key indicators of relaxation and found that meditation provides a far deeper state of relaxation than does simple eyes-closed rest. The research showed that breath rate and plasma lactate decrease, the basal skin resistance increases, significantly more during meditation than during eyes-closed rest. Interestingly, immediately prior to the meditation sessions, meditating subjects had lower levels of breath rate, plasma lactate, spontaneous skin conductance, and heart rate than did the controls. This deeper level of relaxation before starting the practice suggests that reduced physiological stress through meditation is cumulative. American Psychologist, 42: 879-881, 1987.

Improved Perception and Memory

College students instructed in meditation displayed significant improvements in performance over a two-week period on a perceptual and short-term memory test involving the identification of familiar letter sequences presented rapidly. They were compared with subjects randomly assigned to a routine of twice-daily rest with eyes closed, and with subjects who made o change in their daily routine. Memory and Cognition, 10: 207-215, 1982.

Development of Intelligence

University students who regularly practiced meditation increased significantly in intelligences over a two-year period, compared to control subjects. The finding corroborates the results of two other studies showing increased IQ in meditation students. Personality and Individual Differences, 12:1105-1116, 1991, and Perceptual and Motor Skills, 62: 731-738, 1986.

Natural Change in Breathing

Subjects were measured for changes in breathing rate during the practice of meditation. Breath rate fell from 14 breaths per minute to about 11 breaths per minute, indicating meditation produces a state of rest and relaxation. The change in breath rate is natural, effortless, and comfortable. American Journal of Physiology, 22: 795-799, 1971.

Decrease in Stress Hormone

Plasma cortisol is a stress hormone. The study shows that plasma cortisol decreased during meditation, whereas it did not change significantly in controlled subjects during ordinary relaxation. Hormones and Behavior, 10: 54-60, 1978.

Lower Blood Pressure

In a clinical experiment with elderly African American (mean age 66) dwelling in an inner-city community, meditation was compared with the most widely used method of producing physiological relaxation. Subjects who had moderately elevated blood pressure levels were randomly assigned meditation, Progressive Muscle Relaxation (PMR), or usual care. Over a three-month interval, systolic and diastolic blood pressure dropped by 10.6 and 5.9 mm Hg, respectively, in the meditation group, and 4.0 and 2.1 mm Hg in the PMR group, with virtually no change in the usual care group. A second random assignment study with the elderly conducted at Harvard found similar blood pressure changes produced by meditation over three-months (11 mm Hg for systolic blood pressure). Journal of Personality and Social Psychology, 57: 950-964, 1989.

Reversal of Aging Process

Biological age measures how old a person is physiologically. As a group, long-term meditators who had been practicing meditation for more than five years were physiologically twelve years younger than their chronological age, as measured by reduction of blood pressure, and better near-point version and auditory discrimination. Short-term meditators were physiologically five years younger than their chronological age. The study controlled for the effects of diet and exercise. International Journal of Neuroscience, 16: 53-58, 1982.

Reduced Need for Medical Care

A study of health insurance statistics on over 2,000 people practicing meditation over a five-year period found that meditators consistently had less than half the hospitalization than did other groups with comparable age, gender, profession, and insurance terms. The difference between the meditation and non-meditation groups increased in older-age brackets. In addition, the meditators had fewer incidents of illness in seventeen medical treatment categories, including 87% less hospitalization for heart disease and 55% less for cancer. The meditators consistently had more than 50% fewer doctor visits than did other groups. Psychosomatic Medicine, 49: 493-507, 1987.

Cholesterol

A longitudinal study showed that cholesterol levels significantly decreased through meditation in hypercholsteolemic patients, compared to matched controls, over an eleven-month period. Journal of Human Stress, 5: 24-27, 1979.

Increased Self-Actualization

Self-actualization refers to realizing more of one's inner potential, expressed in every area of life. A statistical meta-analysis of 42 independent studies indicated the effect of meditation on increasing self-actualization is markedly greater than that of other forms of relaxation. This analysis statistically controlled the length of treatment and quality of research design. Journal of Social Behavior and Personality, 6: 189-248, 1991.

Increased Strength of Self-Concept

One month after beginning meditation, subjects experienced an improved self-concept in comparison to before learning meditation. Meditation participants developed a more strongly defined self-concept and also came to perceive their "actual self" as significantly closer to their "ideal self." No similar changes were observed for matched controls. Journal of Psychology, 4: 206-218, 1976.

Decreased Cigarette, Alcohol, and Drug Abuse

A statistical meta-analysis of 198 independent treatment outcomes found that meditation produced a significantly larger reduction in tobacco, alcohol, and illicit drug use than either standard substance abuse treatments (including counseling, pharmacological treatments, relaxation training, and Twelve-Step programs) or prevention programs (such as programs to counteract peer-pressure and promote personal development). This meta-analysis controlled for strength of study design and included both heavy and casual users. Whereas, the effects of conventional programs typically decrease sharply by three months, effects of meditation on total abstinence from tobacco, alcohol, and illicit drug ranged from 50% to 89% over a 18 to 22 month period of study. Alcoholism Treatment Quarterly, 11: 13-87, and International Journal of the Addictions, 26: 293-325, 1991.

Increased Productivity

In this study subjects practicing meditation showed significant improvements at work, compared with members of a control group. Job performance and job satisfaction increased while desire to change jobs decreased. People at every level of the organization benefited from practicing meditation. Academy of Management Journal, 17: 362-368, 1974.

Improved Relations at Work

This study found significant improvements in relations with supervisors and co-workers after an average of eleven months practicing meditation, in comparison to control subjects. And while meditators reported that they felt less anxiety about promotion (shown by reduced climb orientation), their fellow employees saw them as moving ahead quickly. People at every level of the organization benefited from practicing meditation. Academy of Management Journal, 17: 362-368, 1974.

Increased Relaxation and Decreased Stress

This three-month study of managers and employees who regularly practiced meditation in a Fortune 100 manufacturing company (Puritan-Bennett Corporation) and a smaller distribution-sales company in Philadelphia showed that meditation practitioners displayed more relaxed physiological functioning, greater reduction in anxiety, and reduced tension on the job, when compared to control subjects with similar job positions in the same companies. Anxiety, Stress and Coping International Journal, 6: 245-262, 1993.

Improved Health and More Positive Health Habits

In two companies that introduced meditation, managers and employees who regularly practiced meditation improved significantly in overall physical health, mental well-being, and vitality when compared to control subjects with similar jobs in the same companies. Meditation practitioners also reported significant reductions in health problems such as headaches and backaches, improved quality of sleep, and a significant reduction in the use of hard liquor and cigarettes, compared to personnel in the control groups. Anxiety, Stress and Coping International Journal, 6: 245-262, 1993.

Discussion

From personal experience, I can say that these kinds of benefits sometimes happen, and even often happen, when people meditate every day, **if** they are doing the right meditation for their individuality.

This life-transforming quality of meditation is not all that mysterious – just imagine how your life would change if you spend 45 minutes a day in the greatest relaxation you have ever known, resting more deeply than sleep, giving your body, nervous system, and brain a chance to tune for action.

So why don't more people meditate? Why do only 10 million Americans meditate? For one thing, there are thousands of different kinds of meditation, and many of them will grate on your nerves. You will only feel at home with certain ones. Many of these other techniques are like kinds of music you just do not like, flavors of food you will never grow to love. You can't do someone else's meditation and you can't live someone else's life.

Keep in mind that meditation (the way I teach it) leads to a kind of restfulness and ease greater than you have ever known. This is a natural experience and you have not been getting it, most likely. So the pervasive benefits which are reported make sense. Often, when a person starts meditating every day, 20 minutes in the morning before breakfast, 20 minutes in the evening before dinner, you can watch them change visibly over the next three months. People start looking more rested and relaxed, as if they just came back from a vacation. They get a kind of glow about them, as if they are in love. I have seen this over and over again in the past 36 years of teaching meditation – it's what keeps me interested in meditation.

The benefits of daily meditation practice are sometimes dramatic, when people find a technique that truly suits their individual nature. This is a big IF, though. There really does have to be a good match between the meditation practice – and there are thousands of techniques and variations – and your unique individual needs and preferences. Otherwise you won't want to meditate, you won't feel comfortable doing the technique, and you won't thrive.

Read the Science For Yourself

If you want to read further in the research, see The Physical and Psychological Effects of Meditation (opens in new window) online at the Institute of Noetic Sciences. I used to hand out thousands of copies of these kinds of research reports at the TM lectures I gave from 1970 to 1975.

With all scientific research, it helps if you know the conditions in the lab and the expectations of the researchers. I was a lab subject for meditation research from 1968 through 1978. One study I was in focused on serum cortisol, a stress hormone. This meant that I was asked to drive over to University of California Medical Center in Irvine or Tustin, and sit in a chair and let Archie Wilson stick needles in my arm to take blood samples. In one of the labs I meditated in, about 30 feet away from the chair I was sitting in, was a wall of cages with white mice or rats in them, and the smell of ether was in the room. The noise, having people in white coats hoovering over me, the stink of the mice, the chemical smells in the room, and having a big catheter in my wrist, all made it a bit challenging to go deep into meditation. The ether in the room may have made me go to sleep for a few seconds here and there during the half hour meditation, I don't know. I normally nod off for a few seconds here and there in meditation. But the overall stress of meditating in such a weird place may have raised my cortisol levels somewhat before meditating, so perhaps there was more of a drop during meditation, which would make for more "before and during contrast." Who knows. Has anyone studied that? So whenever you read the research, especially physiological research on meditation, imagine that someone, God knows why, volunteers to go into a lab and meditate under those conditions. I did it as part of my general evangelism for meditation, because the researchers were desperate for subjects, and because they were friends of mine and when they called I couldn't say no.

Meditating scientists, especially members of the TM organization, conducted much of the early research on meditation (1970-77) and quite a bit of it has not been fully replicated, so you should take these results with a grain of salt. In the late 1970's some scientists got tired of reading all the glowing, evangelical reseach reports on the benefits of meditation and decided to debunk it. So they invited a bunch of meditators to come into their lab and meditate, and they found - voila! - significant amounts of sleep during meditation, much more than anyone else had found. This was published in a journal, and I heard gloating comments from various scientists, ha ha ha, meditation is just sleep, you meditators have really been put in your place. The image is really funny, if you think about it – there is a meditator sitting in a lab, all these instruments wired to her body to measure these supposedly remarkable physiological effects, and then what . . . instead of meditating, she just falls alseep. ZZZZzzzzzz instead of OMmmmmm. Then I happened to be talking with a researcher who had stopped by the lab where this study was conducted, and he found it had a very strong smell of ether, for they were anesthetizing rats nearby and there was quite a strong smell. He said none of the researchers there even noticed the ether smell anymore – they were all used to it. They dismissed the idea that the ether was putting the meditators to sleep. All these things happen during research – scientists are just human, and they want to prove things, and sometimes they want to prove other scientists are wrong.

So there needs to be a study on the effect of small amounts of ether on meditation. And physiologists need to publish more details of how they actually do the studies. In the serum cortisol study I was a subject in, the subtitle should have been, "Effects on serum cortisol of meditating in a room full of rats and ether while needles are stuck in your arm and doctors hoover over you taking blood samples every five minutes."

Any one scientific study does not mean much, except to point out a field of inquiry. The results are often somewhat wrong, and the reasons given for the effect are often wrong. But when many people replicate the results, eventually they figure out what is going on. Right now the only meditation research I give high credibility to is that associated with the Harvard Medical School labs of Herbert Benson and The Mind Body Medical Institute. Benson is a real physician and a scientist, and I don't believe he would publish anything that is not replicable. So when you read the science collated at the Noetic sciences site, check back at MBMI to see what subset of the exploratory studies have been validated.

Science is clear thinking that gets done in spite of the fact that money, politics, and religion are involved. In terms of scientific research, there is a good news/bad news situation. The good news is that meditation is not a drug. It is a built-in instinct of the human body. The bad news is that it not a drug. There is no way for a drug company to make billions of dollars selling meditation pills, so why should they invest millions of dollars doing research on it? Eventually, insurance companies may spend a lot of money on meditation research, because they wind up paying for what happens when people don't meditate. There is another good/bad situation, which is that many researchers are passionate about meditation and figure out how to do low-budget studies. This is interesting. The bad news is that they may skew the results, or try to prove that their type of meditation, whether it be Buddhist, Hindu, or nondemonational, is better, and then the study is not replicated. This will eventually bring dishonor to the field. Science advances through confusion and controversy, but only if people keep working to clarify things.

How Do I Get These Benefits?

You only get the benefits of meditation if you actually meditate everyday – that is one key. And in order to meditate every day, you need to find a technique and an approach that truly suits your individuality and the rhythm of your day. That is where Instinctive Meditation is so useful – because you don't just learn a technique, you learn how to adapt meditation to fit the direction of your life.

What is meditation? It is a skill of paying attention in a restful way to the flow of life in your body. This triggers a natural response, a built-in instinct. There are thousands of different meditation techniques that can serve to elicit a similar physiological response.

Meditation is a built-in capacity of the human body. That means you can do it, and it can feel natural to you. The thousands of different techniques of meditation are just different ways of letting yourself love what you love. Learning to meditate is a matter of learning to cooperate with your individual nature, learning to give in to the way that you love life. Because meditation is invisible behavior, hardly anyone gets coaching. So you need to have some understanding as you set out, so that you get the feel for what it means to go with your own essential nature, rather than go against it.

Here is a simple truth to consider: meditate in accord with your nature. Let your technique be what you love. That is why the term, "instinctive meditation" suggests itself for the path of letting one's inner nature suggest the type and tone of one's meditation practice.

How Do I Learn?

Some people are naturals, and need no instruction. If they need a teacher, it is more to help prevent bad habits from forming.

The best way to get started is one-to-one instruction. about 90 minutes a day for five consecutive days, then every other day for the next week, then once a week for a few weeks. In these sessions, we explore what techniques work the best for you. Then, as you meditate each day, you get immediate feedback on how to handle experiences.

Some people – maybe one in twenty – can just meditate, and need no instruction. Others need a little coaching. Whenever you begin meditation, or begin again, you get a fresh start. All my books are written in such a way that you can start meditating and building the skills you need.

Let's Go

A good way to begin is to use the book and CD, Meditation 24/7: http://www.lorinroche.com/page43/page33/page33.html
It is really short and succinct, and comes with a great CD of 14 guided meditations and awareness exercises.

Study Says Meditation Benefits the Brain

Feb. 6, 2003, HD Lighthouse - Huntington's Disease: information and community
http://www.hdlighthouse.org/treatment-care/care/hdltriad/spirituality/updates/0032meditation.php

MILWAUKEE - For the first time, meditation has been shown to produce lasting beneficial changes in immune-system function as well as brain electrical activity, according to a University of Wisconsin-Madison study released Monday.

The study, which looked at a group of 25 employees of a Madison-area company who underwent an eight-week meditation training program, is the latest in a growing body of research into the mind-body connection.

As a part of the study at the end of the eight weeks, flu shots were given to the employees and a group of 16 other employees who did not receive meditation training.
When researchers checked for antibodies to the vaccine at one month and two months later, the meditators had significantly higher levels than the nonmeditators.

On average, the meditators had about a 5 percent increase in antibodies, but some had increases of up to 25 percent, Davidson said.

More importantly, the level of antibodies increased directly in relation to the level of increased brain-wave activity, he said. To measure brain activity, electroencephalograms were done. Researchers found about 50 percent more electrical activity in the left frontal regions of the brains of the meditators. Other research has showed that part of the brain is associated with positive emotions and anxiety reduction.

The study's findings will be published in the upcoming issue of the journal *Psychosomatic Medicine*.

While many researchers have presumed that the benefits of meditation endure, there has been a shortage of such research, said Andrew Newberg, an assistant professor of radiology at the University of Pennsylvania who has done several neuroimaging studies involving meditation and prayer. "The fact they can show long-term or chronic changes... is not completely surprising, but it's important they were able to show that," he said. "These kinds of studies, when done by high-quality researchers, are really what has been lacking in the field of alternative medicine."

The meditation training for the study was done by **Jon Kabat-Zinn**, a noted meditation author who developed a stress-reduction program at the University of Massachusetts Medical Center.

Judith Stevens, one of the test subjects, said her training has helped her think more clearly and react less emotionally to stressful situations.

"The road rage went down," she said, laughing.
She said she now practices meditation for about 10 to 20 minutes, five times a week.

A weakness of the study is the relatively small number of participants and use of EEG, which is considered a relatively crude measurement of brain function.

# # #

John Davidson

http://www.psychiatry.wisc.edu/Faculty/FacultyPages/Davidson.htm

MIND OVER ARTHRITIS

Mindfulness meditation can help ease the distress of rheumatoid arthritis by increasing mental clarity and calmness.

The pain of rheumatoid arthritis (RA) begins with inflammation and joint damage. But stress and negative emotions can make the pain worse. The most effective relief strategies target both the physical and the mental components of pain.

Mind-body therapies like meditation are increasingly used along with standard treatments for conditions like heart disease, anxiety, and depression. In a recent study, researchers evaluated the potential benefits of a type of meditation known as mindfulness-based stress reduction (MBSR) for people with RA.

Living in the moment

MBSR focuses primarily on increasing mental clarity and calmness. It has been used for many years to help people cope with stress, anxiety, chronic pain, headaches, stomach problems, sleep difficulties, fatigue, and high blood pressure.

The practice involves a moment-to-moment awareness and acceptance of one's thoughts, emotions, and physical sensations. People who practice MBSR learn to view these internal and external experiences in a non-judgmental way, with compassion for themselves and others.

Mindfulness in RA

In a study conducted at the University of Maryland School of Medicine, 63 people with RA were ran-domly assigned to either a group practicing MBSR or a control group. All participants continued their usual medical care. The MBSR group had eight weeks of instruction in the technique, followed by three refresher classes during the next four months. The control group was placed on a waiting list for a future MBSR class.

After six months, individuals who had practiced MBSR showed a 35% reduction in psychological distress and an increased sense of well-being compared with the control group. Their degree of disease activity had not changed.

Lead investigator Elizabeth K. Pradhan, PhD, MPH, assistant professor at the Center for Integrative Medicine at the University of Maryland School of Medicine, notes that practicing MBSR appears to quiet much of the judging that goes on in our minds—thoughts like "This is really bad."

"When you begin to accept life just as it is, without all the judging, what emerges is not just self-acceptance but more acceptance in general," she says. "People just become more at peace with how things are—which is not to say that they give in to their RA. It's more like the RA doesn't become a reason not to be peaceful or happy."

Classes in mindfulness meditation are available around the country. The MBSR program used in the study was developed at the Center for Mindfulness in Medicine, Health Care, and Society at the University of Massachusetts Medical School. The center maintains a list of instructors, by state, at *www.umassmed.edu/cfm/mbsr.*

Source: Arthritis Care & Research

A PSYCHOTHERAPIST TURNS THE POWERS OF THE MIND ON HERSELF

Wina Maria Diana, a practicing psychotherapist in Severn, Maryland, developed RA six years ago after her son was born. She joined Dr. Pradhan's mindfulness-based stress reduction study on the recommendation of her rheumatologist. After five years, she's still meditating, and she enthusiastically recommends it to all her friends and to the people she counsels in her psychotherapy practice.

"It's so much more basic than people think," she says. "It's not about candles and chanting. It's really just a very simple way of being with yourself, of being in the present.

"The concept of being in the present is so powerful for me. It has made a huge difference in the way I react, even when I'm in the worst flare-up pain. I'm sure the pain is just as intense, but it's so much easier to face when you are with it. You're not thinking, 'Is it going to be like this all night? What am I going to do?' Instead, you are very present, and it's very reassuring. If you are just present, there is a sense of peaceful-ness that makes everything better."